WELCOME!

On behalf of Splash! Publications, we would like to welcome you to *Early American Government*, one of several books in our American History series. Since this curriculum was designed by teachers, we are positive that you will find it to be the most comprehensive program you have ever utilized to teach students about Early American Government. We would like to take a few moments to familiarize you with the program.

THE FORMAT

Early American Government is a nine lesson program. Our goal is a curriculum that you can use the very first day you purchase our materials. No lessons to plan, comprehension questions to write, activities to create, or vocabulary words to define. Simply open the book and start teaching.

Each of the nine lessons requires students to complete vocabulary cards, read about a Government topic, complete a comprehension activity that will expose them to various standardized test formats, and answer thought provoking discussion questions. In addition, each lesson includes a balanced mix of lower and higher level activities for students to complete. Vocabulary quizzes, primary and secondary source activities, grid and cardinal direction mapping, time lines, thought provoking discussion questions, and following directions are the types of activities that will guide students through their journey of *Early American Government*.

THE LESSON PLANS

On the next several pages, you will find the Lesson Plans for *Early American Government*. The Lesson Plans clearly outline what students must do before, during, and after each lesson. Page numbers are listed so that you will immediately know what you need to photocopy before beginning each lesson. The answers to all activities, quizzes, and comprehension questions are located on pages 91-94.

THE VOCABULARY

Each lesson features words in bold type. We have included a Glossary on pages 86-90 to help students pronounce and define the words. Unlike a dictionary, the definitions in the Glossary are concise and written in context. Remember, we're teachers! Students will be exposed to these vocabulary words in the comprehension activities. They will also be tested on the vocabulary words five times throughout their study of *Early American Government*.

Students will be responsible for filling out and studying the vocabulary cards. You may want to have students bring in a small box for storing their vocabulary cards. We don't have to tell you that incorporating these words into your Reading and Spelling programs will save time and make the words more meaningful for students.

CORE STANDARDS: THE "BIG IDEAS"

Core Standards help teachers prioritize instruction and connect the "big ideas" students need to know in order to advance. As a reading-based unit, *Early American Government* fosters literacy in Social Studies.

At the same time that students are learning important factual content about *Early American Government*, they are meeting the Common Core Standards for English Language Arts and making connections to the "big ideas" in American History. Alignment to the 3rd-5th Grade Common Core Standards is clearly noted in the Lesson Plans. Below is the legend used to abbreviate the Common Core Strands:

COMMON CORE STRAND CODE:
CC = COMMON CORE
RL = READING-LITERATURE
RI = READING INFORMATIONAL TEXT
RF = READING FOUNDATIONS SKILLS
W = WRITING
SL = SPEAKING LISTENING
L = LANGUAGE

THE COPYRIGHT

OUR OTHER TITLES

COMPLETE STATE HISTORY PROGRAMS
Do American History!
Do Arizona!
Do California!
Do Colorado!
Do Nevada!
Do New Mexico!
Do Texas!
Do Washington!

LITERATURE STUDY GUIDES
Charlotte's Web
Cricket in Times Square
Enormous Egg
Sarah, Plain and Tall

PRIMARY SERIES
Leveled Math: Addition Bk 1
Leveled Math: Addition Bk 2
Leveled Math: Subtraction Bk 1
Leveled Math: Subtraction Bk 2
National Holidays
National Symbols
Poems for Every Holiday
Poems for Every Season

AMERICAN HISTORY SERIES
New World Explorers
Spanish Explorers & Conquistadors
The Thirteen Original Colonies
The American Revolution
Slavery in America
The Civil War
Westward Expansion

U.S. REGION SERIES
The Middle Atlantic States
The New England States
The Great Lakes States
The Great Plains States
The Southeast States
The Southwest States
The Mountain States
The Pacific States

STATE HISTORY SERIES
Arizona Geography
Arizona Animals
Arizona History
Arizona Government & Economy
California Geography
California Animals
California History
California Government & Economy
Florida Geography
Florida Animals
Florida History
Florida Government & Economy
Illinois History
Indiana History
Michigan History
Ohio History
Texas Geography
Texas Animals
Texas History
Texas Government & Economy

TABLE OF CONTENTS

EARLY AMERICAN GOVERNMENT

TABLE OF CONTENTS

EARLY AMERICAN GOVERNMENT (CONTINUED)

LESSONS *at a* GLANCE

1. Before reading Government, students will:
- complete Vocabulary Cards for *accused, ancient, Atlantic Coast, boundaries, citizen, colonists, conflicts, defend, democracy, discriminated, enforce, foreign, income, jury, majority, military, New World, North America, representative.* *(pg. 1)*

After reading Government *(pps. 2-3)*, students will:
- answer Government Reading Comprehension Questions. *(pg. 4)*
- complete Government Discussion Questions. *(pg. 5)*
- take a Vocabulary Quiz for American Government Part I. *(pg. 6)*

THE GOVERNMENT LESSON IS ALIGNED WITH THESE 3RD-5TH GRADE CORE STANDARDS:
CC.RI.1, CC.RI.2, CC.RI.3, CC.RI.4, CC.RI.5, CC.RI.10, CC.RF.3A, CC.RF.4A, CC.RF.4C, CC.W.1A, CC.W.1B, CC.W.9B, CC.L.4A, CC.L.4C, CC.L.6

2. Before reading First Governments in America, students will:
- complete Vocabulary Cards for *archaeologists, Asia, centuries, charters, Church of England, commissioners, confederacy, constitution, council, cultivate, elected, founded, fungus, governor, harsh, historians, independent, inhabited, longhouses, maize, merchants, monarch, New England, official, Pilgrims, prosper, Puritan, Quakers, unanimously, united, vetoed, wigwam.* *(pg. 1)*

After reading First Governments in America *(pps. 7-11)*, students will:
- answer First Governments in America Reading Comprehension Questions. *(pg. 12)*
- complete First Governments in America Discussion Questions. *(pg. 13)*
- take a Vocabulary Quiz for American Government Part II. *(pps. 14-15)*

THE FIRST GOVERNMENTS IN AMERICA LESSON IS ALIGNED WITH THESE 3RD-5TH GRADE CORE STANDARDS: CC.RI.1, CC.RI.2, CC.RI.3, CC.RI.4, CC.RI.5, CC.RI.10, CC.RF.3A, CC.RF.4A, CC.RF.4C, CC.W.1A, CC.W.1B, CC.W.9B, CC.L.4A, CC.L.4C, CC.L.6

LESSONS *at a* GLANCE

3. Before reading The French and Indian War, students will:
- complete Vocabulary Cards for *allies, ambushed, autobiography, biographies, captives, defeat, European, Great Lakes, gristmills, ignored, indigo, New France, outraged, preserve, proclamation, profit, province, raided, reserved, resources, sawmills, seized, surrendered. (pg. 1)*

After reading The French and Indian War *(pps. 16-18)*, students will:
- answer The French and Indian War Reading Comprehension Questions. *(pg. 19)*
- complete French and Indian War Discussion Questions. *(pg. 20)*
- differentiate between primary and secondary sources. *(pg. 21)*
- use a compass rose to create a French and Indian War Battle Map. *(pps. 22-26)*
- take a Vocabulary Quiz for American Government Part III. *(pps. 27-28)*

THE FRENCH AND INDIAN WAR LESSON IS ALIGNED WITH THESE 3RD-5TH GRADE CORE STANDARDS: **CC.RI.1, CC.RI.2, CC.RI.3, CC.RI.4, CC.RI.5, CC.RI.6, CC.RI.7, CC.RI.10, CC.RF.3A, CC.RF.4A, CC.RF.4C, CC.W.1A, CC.W.1B, CC.W.9B, CC.L.4A, CC.L.4C, CC.L.6**

4. Before reading Great Britain's Taxes, students will:
- complete Vocabulary Cards for *boycotting, debt, disguised, hostility, imported, intolerable, prohibited, protest, repealed, revolted. (pg. 1)*

After reading Great Britain's Taxes *(pps. 29-31)*, students will:
- answer Great Britain's Taxes Reading Comprehension Questions. *(pg. 32)*
- complete Great Britain's Taxes Discussion Questions. *(pg. 33)*
- create a Time Line for Great Britain's taxation in Time Travel. *(pps. 34-35)*

THE GREAT BRITAIN'S TAXES LESSON IS ALIGNED WITH THESE 3RD-5TH GRADE CORE STANDARDS: **CC.RI.1, CC.RI.2, CC.RI.3, CC.RI.4, CC.RI.5, CC.RI.6, CC.RI.7, CC.RI.10, CC.RF.3A, CC.RF.4A, CC.RF.4C, CC.W.1A, CC.W.1B, CC.W.9B, CC.L.4A, CC.L.4C, CC.L.6**

LESSONS *at a* GLANCE

5. Before reading The Continental Congress, students will:
- complete Vocabulary Cards for *abolish, architects, Continental Army, delegates, loyalty, militia, minuteman, Patriots, Revolutionary War.* (*pg. 1*)

After reading The Continental Congress (*pps. 36-37*), students will:
- answer The Continental Congress Reading Comprehension Questions. (*pg. 38*)
- complete The Continental Congress Discussion Questions. (*pg. 39*)
- follow written directions to construct a model of Carpenter's Hall. (*pps. 40-53*)

THE CONTINENTAL CONGRESS LESSON IS ALIGNED WITH THESE 3RD-5TH GRADE CORE STANDARDS: CC.RI.1, CC.RI.2, CC.RI.3, CC.RI.4, CC.RI.5, CC.RI.7, CC.RI.10, CC.RF.3A, CC.RF.4A, CC.RF.4C, CC.W.1A, CC.W.1B, CC.W.9B, CC.L.4A, CC.L.4C, CC.L.6

6. Before reading The Declaration of Independence, students will:
- complete Vocabulary Cards for *adopt, debate, overturn, rebel, transported, traitors, voyage.* (*pg. 1*)

After reading The Declaration of Independence (*pps. 54-55*), students will:
- answer The Declaration of Independence Reading Comprehension Questions. (*pg. 56*)
- complete The Declaration of Independence Discussion Questions. (*pg. 57*)

THE DECLARATION OF INDEPENDENCE LESSON IS ALIGNED WITH THESE 3RD-5TH GRADE CORE STANDARDS: CC.RI.1, CC.RI.2, CC.RI.3, CC.RI.4, CC.RI.5, CC.RI.6, CC.RI.7, CC.RI.10, CC.RF.3A, CC.RF.4A, CC.RF.4C, CC.W.1A, CC.W.1B, CC.W.9B, CC.L.4A, CC.L.4C, CC.L.6

LESSONS *at a* GLANCE

7. Before reading The Articles of Confederation, students will:
  • complete Vocabulary Cards for *interfere and federal government.* *(pg. 1)*

After reading The Articles of Confederation *(pps. 58-59)*, students will:
  • answer The Articles of Confederation Reading Comprehension Questions. *(pg. 60)*
  • complete The Articles of Confederation Discussion Questions. *(pg. 61)*
  • take a Vocabulary Quiz for American Government Part IV. *(pps. 62-63)*

THE ARTICLES OF CONFEDERATION LESSON IS ALIGNED WITH THESE 3RD-5TH GRADE CORE STANDARDS:
CC.RI.1, CC.RI.2, CC.RI.3, CC.RI.4, CC.RI.5, CC.RI.10, CC.RF.3A, CC.RF.4A, CC.RF.4C,
CC.W.1A, CC.W.1B, CC.W.9B, CC.L.4A, CC.L.4C, CC.L.6

8. Before reading The United States Constitution, students will:
  • complete Vocabulary Cards for *abused, appealed, appointed, archives, artifacts,*
    capital, census, civil, conserving, convinced, cultures, donations, economy,
    engraves, estate, exhibits, helium, illegal, justice, monopolies, mourned, outlawed,
    plantations, population, promoted, ratify, respected, retiring, Supreme Court,
    surveying, welfare. *(pg. 1)*

After reading The United States Constitution *(pps. 64-68)*, students will:
  • answer The United States Constitution Reading Comprehension Questions. *(pg. 69)*
  • complete The United States Constitution Discussion Questions. *(pg. 70)*
  • read about George Washington and answer thought provoking questions. *(pps. 71-73)*
  • use a grid system to create a map of the National Mall in Washington, D.C. *(pps. 74-79)*

THE UNITED STATES CONSTITUTION LESSON IS ALIGNED WITH THESE 3RD-5TH GRADE CORE STANDARDS:
CC.RI.1, CC.RI.2, CC.RI.3, CC.RI.4, CC.RI.5, CC.RI.7, CC.RI.10, CC.RF.3A, CC.RF.4A,
CC.RF.4C, CC.W.1A, CC.W.1B, CC.W.9B, CC.L.4A, CC.L.4C, CC.L.6

LESSONS *at a* GLANCE

9.   Before reading The Bill of Rights, students will:
  • complete Vocabulary Cards for *amendments, bail, innocent, press, sued, testify, warrant.* *(pg. 1)*

After reading The Bill of Rights *(pps. 80-81)*, students will:
  • answer The Bill of Rights Reading Comprehension Questions. *(pg. 82)*
  • complete The Bill of Rights Discussion Questions. *(pg. 83)*
  • take a Vocabulary Quiz for American Government Part IV. *(pps. 84-85)*

THE BILL OF RIGHTS LESSON IS ALIGNED WITH THESE 3RD-5TH GRADE CORE STANDARDS: CC.RI.1, CC.RI.2, CC.RI.3, CC.RI.4, CC.RI.5, CC.RI.6, CC.RI.10, CC.RF.3A, CC.RF.4A, CC.RF.4C, CC.W.1A, CC.W.1B, CC.W.9B, CC.L.4A, CC.L.4C, CC.L.6

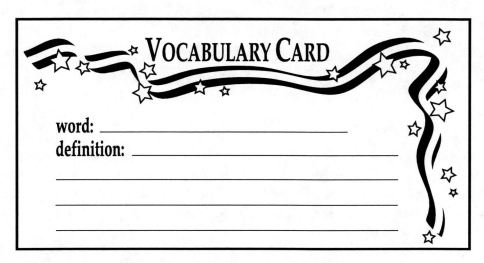

Vocabulary Card

word: _____

definition: _____

_____

_____

_____

Vocabulary Card

word: _____

definition: _____

_____

_____

_____

Vocabulary Card

word: _____

definition: _____

_____

_____

_____

GOVERNMENT

It takes many people to make sure that our nation runs smoothly and everyone gets the protection he or she deserves. Imagine what America must have been like when the first Spanish, French, and English explorers arrived. The land belonged to the country whose explorer claimed it first. If the explorer didn't stay to **defend** the land, the next explorer could come and take the land for his country.

In the late 1500s, the first English **colonists** arrived. The colonists claimed land along the **Atlantic Coast** of **North America**. They built houses and started farming. The colonists could pretty much do as they pleased. As more people arrived in the **New World**, they also claimed land wherever they wanted. There was no weekly trash collection. People threw their garbage in the streets and rivers. There were no property **boundaries**. Farm animals roamed wherever they pleased.

In colonial times, people could be **discriminated** against for any reason at any time. If your skin was a different color, you spoke a **foreign** language, or you didn't have the same religious beliefs as others, you could be forced to leave a town. When arguments broke out, they were settled with fists and guns. The biggest and meanest people usually got what they wanted. There were no rules in place, so people took whatever they wanted. Nobody felt safe.

Fortunately, things have changed. There are people who make the laws, people who **enforce** the laws, and others who make sure law breakers are punished. These people are all part of our government.

WHAT IS GOVERNMENT?

Government is a word used to describe a system of rules. If asked, most of us would say that we don't like rules. There are many reasons why we need the rules that government offers. Settling **conflicts**, making laws, and providing protection are three very powerful reasons for government.

Pretend for a moment that you are on the playground enjoying a game of kickball with your friends. A group of bigger kids approaches, takes the ball, and demands that you leave the field so they can play. If you don't leave immediately, they threaten to hurt you. Since you are smaller, it doesn't make a lot of sense to stay and fight. You could leave, but that wouldn't be fair to you and your friends. You search for an adult who can help you with this problem. You need someone to help you settle the argument fairly, enforce the rules, and protect you from these big bullies. That is an example of government at work.

PAYING TAXES

Government can force people to do things that they might not do on their own. We need schools, parks, libraries, highways, bridges, and a strong **military** to protect us from our enemies. To raise the money to pay for these things, the government forces us to pay taxes. The government takes part of the pay your parents receive for working. This is called **income** tax. When we buy something at the store, we pay a sales tax. The government also raises money by taxing us on the property that we own. When we rent a car to go on vacation, fly on a plane, or stay in a hotel, taxes are collected. All of this money pays for services and other things that we all use.

THE HISTORY OF DEMOCRACY

The word **democracy** comes from two Greek words that mean "people" and "rule." Democracy began a long time ago in the **ancient** Greek city-states of Athens and Sparta. To the Greeks, democracy meant that every **citizen** helped run the city-state. Many people lived in Athens and Sparta, but they weren't all citizens. Women, black slaves, and people who didn't own land were not citizens.

In most democracies today, every adult citizen can vote, but very few people have a hand in actually running the government. In Athens and Sparta, every one who could vote played a direct role in running the government. That's a lot of people making decisions!

GOVERNMENT IN THE UNITED STATES

In the United States, we have a **representative** democracy. This type of government puts the people in charge. In a representative democracy, the **majority** rules. As citizens of the United States, we vote for the leaders we want to represent us.

Establishing a representative democracy in America was not easy. Making rules and collecting taxes did not always make people happy. The first settlers weren't always interested in living by rules or giving part of their hard earned money to the government.

The meaning of democracy has changed over the years. Just like in ancient Athens and Sparta, women, black slaves, and people who didn't own property were not permitted to vote in the early days of the United States. In a democracy, everyone should be treated equally. During the next lesson, we will travel back to the 1500s and learn how our representative democracy started.

FAST FACTS

★ In Athens, the Assembly made the laws. Every citizen was a member of the Assembly. This meant that up to 45,000 people could vote on whether or not a law should be passed.

★ 6,000 people had to be present before a meeting of the Assembly could even begin.

★ If you were **accused** of a crime in Athens, you could have as many as 500 people on the **jury** deciding if you were innocent or guilty. Juries in the United States usually have 12 or fewer members on them.

Name _____

Directions: Read each question carefully. Darken the circle for the correct answer.

---

1 **In the 1500s, which country claimed land along the Atlantic Coast of North America?**

   A France

   B Spain

   C England

   D Russia

2 **In colonial times, if your skin was a different color or you spoke a foreign language, you were <u>probably</u> –**

   F given free land on which to farm

   G forced to leave the colony

   H put in charge of the colony

   J welcomed into the colony

3 **Which phrase <u>best</u> describes the meaning of government?**

   A rules for discrimination

   B groups of people in charge who want to hurt us

   C rules for making and enforcing laws

   D taking someone without permission

4 **Why does the government force us to pay taxes?**

   F The government wants to make us angry.

   G The United States needs things that everyone must help pay for.

   H Rich people need to be punished for making too much money, so the government forces them to pay taxes.

   J The government doesn't want us to have too much money.

5 **Which two Greek words mean democracy?**

   A choose and select

   B protect and punish

   C enforce and defend

   D people and rule

6 **In ancient Athens and Sparta, the decisions were made by –**

   F women

   G black slaves

   H all citizens

   J all men

7 **After reading about government in the United States, you learn that –**

   A our leaders are chosen for us by England

   B we chose to become a representative democracy because it was easy

   C in some ways, our early government was like the government in Athens and Sparta

   D the first colonists wanted more rules and lots of taxes

Answers   **READING**

1 Ⓐ Ⓑ Ⓒ Ⓓ   5 Ⓐ Ⓑ Ⓒ Ⓓ

2 Ⓕ Ⓖ Ⓗ Ⓙ   6 Ⓕ Ⓖ Ⓗ Ⓙ

3 Ⓐ Ⓑ Ⓒ Ⓓ   7 Ⓐ Ⓑ Ⓒ Ⓓ

4 Ⓕ Ⓖ Ⓗ Ⓙ

Name _____

Our government in the United States is in charge of making rules and providing protection for people. Read the questions below about government. Write your answers on the lines provided. Attach a separate piece of paper if you need more room. Be ready to discuss some of your answers.

- **Rules and laws are created to protect us from being hurt or hurting ourselves or others.**

  What is an example of a rule that you have at school or at home?

  _____

  _____

  How does this rule protect you or those around you? _____

  _____

  _____

  If you could change a school or home rule, which one would you change? Explain your reason for changing this rule.

  _____

  _____

  _____

- **In a democracy, everyone should be treated equally.**

  Do you think that we are doing a good job in the United States of treating everyone equally? Explain why you feel this way.

  _____

  _____

  _____

Name _____

Directions: Match the vocabulary word on the left with its definition on the right. Put the letter for the definition on the blank next to the vocabulary word it matches. Use each word and definition only once.

1. _____ accused

2. _____ military

3. _____ majority

4. _____ ancient

5. _____ jury

6. _____ New World

7. _____ boundaries

8. _____ citizen

9. _____ income

10. _____ foreign

11. _____ enforce

12. _____ defend

13. _____ democracy

14. _____ discriminated

15. _____ colonists

16. _____ conflicts

17. _____ Atlantic Coast

18. _____ North America

19. _____ representative

A. more than half.

B. a type of government that gives the people the power to elect leaders who will make and enforce laws.

C. from another country or nation.

D. a term once used to describe the continents of North America and South America.

E. treated some people better or worse than others without a good reason.

F. to keep safe from danger, attack, or harm.

G. one of seven continents in the world. Bounded by Alaska on the northwest, Greenland on the northeast, Florida on the southeast, and Mexico on the southwest.

H. people who are part of the armed forces who may be asked to go to war.

I. money earned from doing work or owning property.

J. struggles or disagreements.

K. a group of people who are chosen to listen to all of the facts during a court case before making a judgment for guilt or innocence.

L. people who are ruled by another country.

M. dividing lines.

N. the area of land that borders the Atlantic Ocean.

O. a person in a city, town, state, or country who enjoys the freedom to vote and participate in government decisions.

P. a person chosen to speak or act for an entire group.

Q. blamed or charged with a crime.

R. require someone to obey the rules.

S. a very long time ago.

FIRST GOVERNMENTS IN AMERICA

Long before explorers and English colonists arrived in the New World, the area was already **inhabited** by millions of Native Americans who spoke thousands of different languages. **Archaeologists** (ar•kee•OL•uh•jists) believe that these people were hunters from the continent of **Asia**. They entered North America by walking across the Bering Land Bridge.

The "bridge" was actually a strip of frozen water that was 1,000 miles wide. It connected northeast Asia to western Alaska thousands of years ago. Wild animals crossed back and forth over the Bering Land Bridge. The Asian people followed the animals into North America. When the ice melted, it raised the level of the sea. The people who followed the animals into North America had no way to get back to Asia. They continued following the wild animals throughout North America. Some of these people settled in the same area that the English colonists would one day claim for themselves.

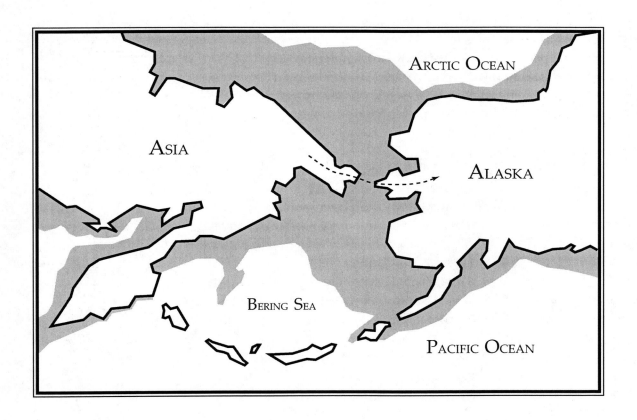

THE IROQUOIS NATION

Tribes that spoke the Iroquois (EAR•uh•kwoy) language were hunters who lived in the Ohio River Valley. They were the largest and most feared group of Native Americans in this area. Iroquois men fished and hunted wild animals and birds. Women planted crops of **maize**, beans, and squash. The Iroquois built **longhouses** that were 20 feet wide and up to 200 feet in length. The longhouses were made of bark and logs and as many as ten families shared one longhouse at the same time.

The Iroquois created the first representative democracy **centuries** before the first English colonists arrived. Remember, in a representative democracy, the citizens are in charge of choosing leaders to represent them. The Iroquois called themselves the League of Five Nations. The Mohawk, Seneca, Oneida (oh•NIE•duh), Cayuga (kay•YOU•guh), and Onondaga (on•un•DAW•guh) were the members of the League of Five Nations.

The Iroquois Nation wrote their own **constitution**. It was known as the Great Binding Law. They created the Great **Council** where representatives from each of the five nations were **elected** by the women of the tribes. Every decision made by the Great Council had to be agreed upon **unanimously** by representatives from each nation. This kept any one nation from becoming more powerful than another. Many **historians** believe that the system of government we have in the United States today was modeled after the Iroquois system.

THE FIRST ENGLISH COLONIES

In 1585 and again in 1587, England tried to establish its first colonies in the **New England** region of America. Both colonies failed. The colonists were completely unprepared for the **harsh** weather. They didn't know how to find food or plant crops in New England's rocky soil. Colonists from one of England's first colonies completely disappeared. What happened to them is still a mystery to this day.

THE JAMESTOWN COLONY

In 1600, England was ready to try establishing another colony. A group of wealthy **merchants** from London believed that they could make a lot of money in America. The businessmen formed the Virginia Company of London. They offered to pay the way of anyone who wanted to go to America.

To repay the merchants, the colonists had to give the Virginia Company part of any gold or silver found in the New World. The colonists were also told to **cultivate** mulberry trees so they could raise silkworms and trade silk with England. The wealthy merchants hired 27 year old John Smith to run the new colony.

In 1607, John Smith and a group of more than 100 men and boys landed near the Chesapeake Bay in present-day Virginia. In honor of England's King James I, they named their colony Jamestown.

JOHN SMITH

THE POWHATAN CONFEDERACY

John Smith found that Jamestown was already inhabited by Native Americans. The Woodland people, led by Chief Powhatan, were part of the Powhatan **Confederacy**.

The Powhatan Confederacy included at least 30 tribes that spoke the Algonquian (al•GONG•kee•in) language. These tribes lived in **wigwam** villages near the coast. John Smith wrote that there were about 100 families in each village. Each village was led by a chief. In the beginning, the Jamestown colonists had a difficult time surviving and getting along with the Native Americans.

The colonists were unable to find gold. A **fungus** destroyed the mulberry trees. All of the silkworms died. The colonists did not know how to hunt, where to fish, or how to make the water pure so they could drink it. They were also unable to protect themselves from disease-carrying mosquitoes. To make matters worse, they were constantly at war with the Native Americans.

In 1608, a supply ship arrived from England. Less than 50 settlers were still alive. In 1609, John Smith was badly injured in a gunpowder explosion. He left Virginia and returned to England for medical care.

CHIEF POWHATAN

THE HOUSE OF BURGESSES (BUR•JIS•IZ)

In 1614, Jamestown colonist John Rolfe married the daughter of Chief Powhatan. Her name was Pocahontas. The marriage brought some peace between the Jamestown settlers and the Native Americans. The Native Americans taught the settlers how to grow tobacco. By 1619, things had changed for the colonists. Sir Thomas Dale and Sir George Yeardley were chosen to lead the colony. The Jamestown Colony began to **prosper**.

The Virginia Company was pleased with the positive changes in the colony. Women were sent to Jamestown to marry the men. Each settler was given a piece of land on which to grow tobacco. The colonists elected 22 representatives who began making laws for the colony. This group of lawmakers was known as the House of Burgesses.

A **governor** for the colony was chosen by the London Company. The governor selected six colonists to serve on his council. The representatives for the House of Burgesses were elected by white males over the age of 17 who owned land.

The House of Burgesses made the laws for the colony. The laws could be **vetoed** by the governor, the council, and the London Company. In 1624, Virginia became a royal colony. The king of England chose a governor for Virginia. As a royal colony, the powers of the House of Burgesses were very limited. The representatives could still make laws, but the king's chosen governor could veto them.

THE PILGRIMS

In 1620, the English **founded** their second permanent settlement in North America. The colonists were known as **Pilgrims**. We call them Pilgrims today, but they didn't actually receive that name until they had been in America for almost 200 years.

Before coming to America, the Pilgrims were **Puritan** farmers in England. The **Church of England** was England's **official** church. Puritans did not agree with the strict rules of the Church of England.

Puritans based their lives on the Bible. They believed that human beings needed God's forgiveness to get them to heaven. They also believed that they were chosen by God to become leaders in government.

The Church of England did not agree with the Puritans' beliefs. Puritans wanted to find a place where they could worship freely and make important decisions.

THE PLYMOUTH COLONY

On September 6, 1620, the Pilgrims left England and sailed for America on *The Mayflower*. They were led by William Brewster. Brewster was a Puritan preacher who received money from the London Company to start a colony in America. Again, in return for the money, Brewster and his group promised to give the London Company part of any gold or silver found in America.

The London Company wanted William Brewster to sail toward Virginia. Stormy weather knocked *The Mayflower* off course. The Pilgrims landed in Massachusetts Bay instead of Virginia. They named their new colony Plymouth. This name was in honor of the city in England from which they had come.

THE MAYFLOWER COMPACT

The Pilgrims didn't have permission from the London Company to settle in Massachusetts. Before leaving their ship, they wrote the Mayflower Compact. This important document established rules and laws for the settlers to obey. It was signed by each of the 41 men aboard *The Mayflower*. The signers believed that laws were to be honored between God and man and between each other. The Mayflower Compact contained fair and equal laws for the settlement. Power was given to the majority.

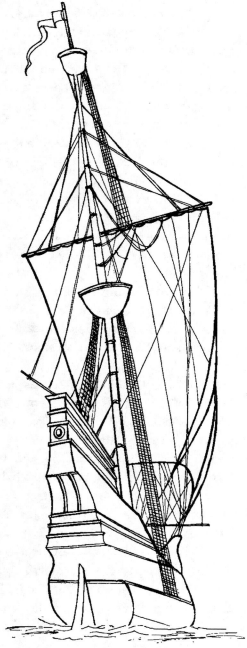

THE MAYFLOWER

THE FUNDAMENTAL ORDERS OF CONNECTICUT

In 1636, Puritan preacher Thomas Hooker founded a colony in Connecticut. Within a short time, Hooker's group built the towns of Hartford, Wethersfield, and Windsor.

In 1639, the three towns **united** as one colony. They wrote their own set of laws known as the Fundamental Orders of Connecticut. Some believe that this was the first written constitution in the New World.

The Fundamental Orders established an **independent** government that made laws for elections, courts, powers of officials, and taxes. It gave all white men who owned land the right to vote.

GREAT LAW OF PENNSYLVANIA

In 1682, William Penn arrived in Pennsylvania with 100 **Quakers**. Quakers refused to fight in war or pay taxes that were used to support war.

William Penn believed that all people were created equal. He established the Great Law of Pennsylvania. Men who believed in God and owned property were given the right to vote.

William Penn also created the County Commission. **Commissioners** were elected officials in charge of keeping peace.

ATLANTIC OCEAN

NEW ENGLAND COLONIES

MIDDLE COLONIES

SOUTHERN COLONIES

OTHER ENGLISH COLONIES

In all, the English **monarch** granted **charters** to individuals and companies who founded thirteen successful colonies in America. They included five New England colonies, four Middle colonies, and five Southern colonies. You will soon learn how these thirteen original colonies became the first thirteen states.

Name _____

Directions: Read each question carefully. Darken the circle for the correct answer.

1 According to the first paragraph of First Governments in America, the first people in North America were –

   A Spanish explorers

   B wild animals

   C hunters from Asia

   D American soldiers

2 How did these people enter North America?

   F They swam across the Arctic Ocean.

   G They crossed a frozen bridge of ice.

   H They flew on Alaskan Airlines.

   J They traveled by boat.

3 After reading about the Iroquois Nation, you can conclude that –

   A they were weak people afraid of everyone

   B each family lived in its own straw hut

   C our early leaders must have studied the Iroquois system of government very closely

   D the Iroquois men had all of the power within the tribe

4 Which statement about the Jamestown Colony is <u>true</u>?

   F They needed the Native Americans to teach them how to survive.

   G They didn't have a leader.

   H They paid their own way America.

   J They knew exactly where to hunt and fish.

5 In the House of Burgesses, the representative were chosen by –

   A the chief of the Powhatan Confederacy

   B the king of England

   C white men over the age of 17 who owned land

   D all of the Jamestown colonists

6 Which group of people came to America in search of religious freedom?

   F The Pilgrims

   G The Powhatan Confederacy

   H The Iroquois Nation

   J The Virginia Company

7 Which of the following gave men who believed in God and owned property the right to vote?

   A The Mayflower Compact

   B The House of Burgesses

   C The Fundamental Orders of Connecticut

   D The Great Law of Pennsylvania

READING

Answers

1 Ⓐ Ⓑ Ⓒ Ⓓ   5 Ⓐ Ⓑ Ⓒ Ⓓ
2 Ⓕ Ⓖ Ⓗ Ⓙ   6 Ⓕ Ⓖ Ⓗ Ⓙ
3 Ⓐ Ⓑ Ⓒ Ⓓ   7 Ⓐ Ⓑ Ⓒ Ⓓ
4 Ⓕ Ⓖ Ⓗ Ⓙ

Name _____

FIRST GOVERNMENTS IN AMERICA

During the 1500s, the first colonists made the dangerous journey across the Atlantic Ocean to settle in the New World. Read the questions below about the first colonists. Write your answers on the lines provided. Attach a separate piece of paper if you need more room. Be ready to discuss some of your answers.

- **Sailing to America was a 3,000-mile journey that took more than two months.**

  Was it worth it? If you had been a colonist traveling to America, what would have been the costs and benefits of making the trip?

  Costs: _____

  _____

  Benefits: _____

  _____

  Now decide whether you think it was worth making the trip. Explain your answer.

  _____

  _____

  _____

- **The first governments established by the colonists only allowed white men who owned property the privilege of voting.**

  Why do you think the first governments did not include women, men who didn't own land, or blacks in the voting process? Do you agree? Explain.

  _____

  _____

  _____

  _____

✦ VOCABULARY QUIZ ✦
EARLY AMERICAN GOVERNMENT
PART II

Directions: Match the vocabulary word on the left with its definition on the right. Put the letter for the definition on the blank next to the vocabulary word it matches. Use each word and definition only once.

1. _____ wigwam

2. _____ vetoed

3. _____ Asia

4. _____ centuries

5. _____ united

6. _____ archaeologists

7. _____ maize

8. _____ unanimously

9. _____ commissioners

10. _____ confederacy

11. _____ Quakers

12. _____ Puritan

13. _____ prosper

14. _____ Pilgrims

A. government officials in charge of a department.

B. lived or settled in a place.

C. long dwellings where many Native American families live at the same time.

D. a disease that destroys plants.

E. a Native American home made of poles and covered with bark, mats, or animal skins.

F. buyers and sellers whose goal is to make money.

G. not being under the control or rule of someone else.

H. periods of 100 years.

I. very uncomfortable conditions.

J. the official church in England.

K. joined together and formed a single unit.

L. people who study the past.

M. a group of people chosen to make laws or give advice.

N. contracts which give one group power over another.

O. prevented a bill from becoming a law.

15. _____ constitution

16. _____ official

17. _____ monarch

18. _____ merchants

19. _____ council

20. _____ cultivate

21. _____ longhouses

22. _____ elected

23. _____ inhabited

24. _____ independent

25. _____ historians

26. _____ founded

27. _____ harsh

28. _____ Church of England

29. _____ fungus

30. _____ governor

31. _____ charters

32. _____ New England

P. the English colonists who founded the first permanent settlement in the New England colony of Plymouth in 1620.

Q. a group of people with common goals.

R. a type of corn.

S. selected leaders by voting for them.

T. a person from England who traveled to America in the 1600s and 1700s in search of religious freedom.

U. a king, queen, or emperor who rules for his or her entire life and then passes the role onto his or her child.

V. a region in the northeast corner of the United States that includes Connecticut, Maine, Massachusetts, New Hampshire, Rhode Island, and Vermont.

W. members of a religious group who believed all men were created equal, refused to serve in the army or navy, and would not pay taxes used to support war.

X. a person who is in charge of an area or group.

Y. to have success or wealth.

Z. scientists who study past human life by looking at prehistoric fossils and tools.

AA. the world's largest continent with more than half of the Earth's population.

BB. to prepare the soil for growing crops.

CC. a plan that outlines the duties of government and guarantees the rights of the people.

DD. completely agreed upon by everyone.

EE. proper or correct.

FF. started or established.

THE FRENCH AND INDIAN WAR

During the 1600s and 1700s, many things changed in the country of England and its colonies in America. In 1707, England and Scotland united to form the Kingdom of Great Britain. In 1733, the last of the thirteen original colonies was established. The colonists had built towns, organized governments, and used the **resources** that America offered.

The New England colonists built ships and used their location on the Atlantic Ocean to ship products to other colonies and Great Britain. The settlers in the Middle colonies learned how to turn water from the Hudson and Delaware rivers into energy that could be used in their **sawmills** and **gristmills**. In the Southern colonies, black slaves helped the colonists become wealthy tobacco, wheat, rice, and **indigo** farmers.

BEAVER FURS

The English colonists weren't the only settlers in the New World. While the English colonists established permanent settlements along the Atlantic Ocean, French colonists settled in the **Great Lakes** area. Both groups were interested in gaining more land for their countries. They also wanted to take control of the beaver hunting and trading territories.

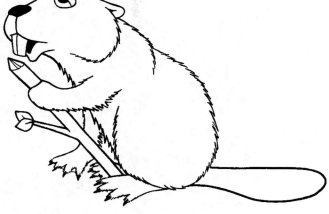

Beaver furs were worth a lot of money to the French and English colonists. The smooth, waterproof beaver furs were shipped back to France and Great Britain where they were sold for a very high **profit**. The furs were used to make expensive beaver hats and coats.

Native Americans in the Great Lakes area trapped and traded with the French colonists. Native Americans who lived along the Atlantic Ocean trapped and traded with the English colonists. The colonists gave the Native Americans **European** goods, metal tools, and weapons. These were items the Native Americans had never seen before. Of course, all of the Native Americans wanted to trade with the colonists. There simply wasn't enough beaver for everyone to hunt and trade. Battles often broke out. The biggest and most powerful tribes usually won.

THE FRENCH AND INDIAN WAR

Everyone wanted control of the Ohio River Valley. It was full of beaver.
The French and English colonists began building forts in the Ohio River Valley. Soldiers
were trained. In 1754, the first battle of the French and Indian War was fought in present-day
Pennsylvania. The French and their Native American **allies** were too strong for young George
Washington and his small army of untrained colonists.

Great Britain sent 1,000 soldiers to help the colonists win the French and Indian War.
Spain sent soldiers to help France. It took six long years, but in 1760, France **surrendered** the
war to Great Britain and its colonists in America.

THE TREATY OF PARIS

In 1763, the French and Indian War officially ended with the Treaty of Paris. The
treaty was signed by Great Britain, France, and Spain. France gave all of its land east of the
Mississippi River, except for New Orleans, to Great Britain. Great Britain also received most
of France's land in Canada. Control of the five Great Lakes and all of the valuable hunting
territories now belonged to Great Britain. The treaty also required Spain to give its territory in
Florida to Great Britain. In return for helping them during the war, France gave New Orleans
and its territory west of the Mississippi River to Spain. The French and Indian War was finally
over.

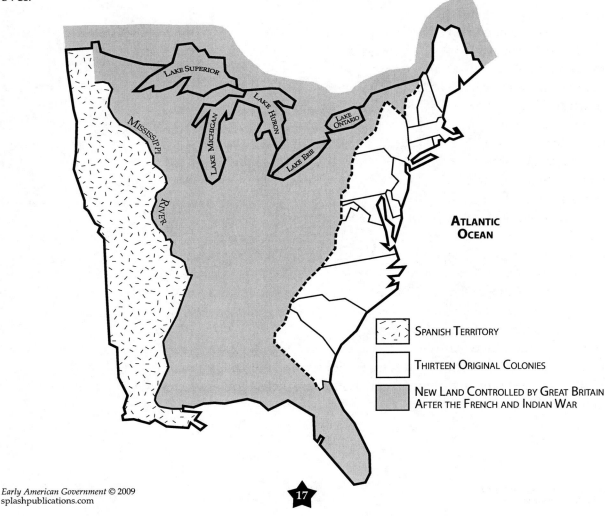

THE ROYAL PROCLAMATION OF 1763

The colonists were eager to explore and settle Great Britain's new land. The leaders in Great Britain were more interested in continuing the profitable fur trade with the Native Americans. The Native Americans were angry that Great Britain and the colonists had won the war. They **raided** settlements, burned British forts, and kidnapped children. To keep peace between the Native Americans and the colonists, King George III decided to separate them from each other.

On October 7, 1763, King George III issued the Royal **Proclamation**. He **reserved** the land west of the Appalachian (ap•uh•LAY•shun) Mountains for Native Americans. Great Britain called this the "Proclamation Line." The colonists were not permitted to settle in this area. All colonists living west of the Appalachian Mountains were ordered to move immediately.

Great Britain sent 10,000 troops to keep the colonists away from the Proclamation Line. The leaders in Great Britain hoped that the Proclamation Line would end the conflicts between the colonists and the Native Americans.

The Royal Proclamation of 1763 gave the Native Americans hope. The Native Americans believed that Great Britain finally realized that they owned land in America.

The colonists were **outraged** by the Royal Proclamation of 1763. They had fought in the French and Indian War to win the land that King George III was simply giving to the Native Americans. The Proclamation Line was **ignored** by the colonists. Hunters and fur trappers from Virginia and North Carolina crossed the Proclamation Line. They planned to build permanent homes west of the Appalachian Mountains.

Mississippi River

· · · · ·   RESERVED FOR NATIVE AMERICANS

RESERVED FOR COLONISTS

- - - - -   PROCLAMATION LINE

Name _____

Directions: Read each question carefully. Darken the circle for the correct answer.

---

1 In 1707, which two countries united to form the Kingdom of Great Britain?

A England and Scotland

B Spain and France

C Asia and the United States

D England and Spain

2 Besides the desire for more land, what actually started the French and Indian War?

F The colonists' desire for independence from Great Britain.

G Black slaves in the New World declared war on the colonists.

H Spain wanted to take control of the English colonies.

J The desire to control the beaver hunting and trading territories.

3 Who helped the colonists win the French and Indian War?

A France and their Native American allies

B British soldiers

C Spanish soldiers

D Russian soldiers

4 What can you learn from studying the Treaty of Paris map?

F The Mississippi River was west of the Spanish Territory.

G The thirteen original colonies were west of the Mississippi River.

H The Great Lakes are northeast of the Mississippi River.

J Spain's territory was east of the thirteen original colonies.

5 After reading about the Royal Proclamation of 1763, you can conclude that –

A the colonists did not want France's land

B the Treaty of Paris awarded the Great Lakes area to Spain

C Great Britain and the colonists disagreed about what to do with the new land

D the land awarded by the Treaty of Paris was worthless

6 What was the importance of the Proclamation Line?

F It was a line that wild animals would not cross.

G It was the new boundary between France and Great Britain.

H It was a line showing where a new town was going to be built.

J It was a line separating the colonists from the Native Americans.

7 The Proclamation Line was _____ of the 13 original colonies.

A north

B south

C east

D west

READING

Answers

1 Ⓐ Ⓑ Ⓒ Ⓓ   5 Ⓐ Ⓑ Ⓒ Ⓓ
2 Ⓕ Ⓖ Ⓗ Ⓙ   6 Ⓕ Ⓖ Ⓗ Ⓙ
3 Ⓐ Ⓑ Ⓒ Ⓓ   7 Ⓐ Ⓑ Ⓒ Ⓓ
4 Ⓕ Ⓖ Ⓗ Ⓙ

Name _____

THE FRENCH AND INDIAN WAR

The French and Indian War was a battle over hunting and trading territories. Read the questions below about the French and Indian War. Write your answers on the lines provided. Attach a separate piece of paper if you need more room. Be ready to discuss some of your answers.

- **Winning the French and Indian War gave Great Britain and its colonists control over the land east of the Mississippi River.**

  If Great Britain had lost the French and Indian War, how do you think it would have changed the history of the United States? Explain your answer.

  _____

  _____

  _____

- **After the Treaty of Paris, King George III kept the colonists out of Native American territory with the Proclamation Line.**

  In your opinion, was the Proclamation Line fair to the colonists? Explain.

  _____

  _____

  _____

  The colonists did not obey the Proclamation Line and crossed it anyway. We have unwanted people crossing into our country all the time. If you had been King George III, what would you have done to keep the colonists from crossing the Proclamation Line? Would that same idea work today?

  _____

  _____

  _____

  _____

the source

Think about the resources we use to learn about history. Reading books, seeing movies, looking at photographs, studying maps, searching the Internet, digging for bones, and holding pieces of pottery are some of the ways that we learn about the past.

There are two types of sources to help us learn about what happened in the past. Primary sources are recorded by people who were there at the time. If you have ever read a diary or an **autobiography**, then you were reading something that was written by the person who was actually recording the events and experiences as they were happening. Diaries and autobiographies are primary sources. Letters, interviews, photographs, original maps, bones, and pieces of pottery are other examples of primary sources because they give us "first-hand" knowledge of an event that took place in history.

Secondary sources are recorded by people after an event took place. Many books have been written about important historical events and people. A book written in 2005 about the life of Jamestown settler John Smith is a secondary source because the author wasn't actually there to interview the famous colonist and can't give any "first-hand" knowledge. Movies, **biographies,** newspaper stories, and encyclopedias are other examples of secondary sources because they give us "second-hand" knowledge of events that took place in history.

You have just finished studying about the beginnings of our government and the French and Indian War.

In this activity, you will decide whether a source of information is a primary source or a secondary source. On the lines provided, put a "P" next to the primary sources and an "S" next to the secondary sources.

1. _____ An encyclopedia article written about the government in Athens and Sparta.

2. _____ The diary of a French soldier written during the French and Indian War.

3. _____ George Washington's autobiography.

4. _____ The actual letter written to the colonists from King George III.

5. _____ The original Fundamental Orders of Connecticut.

6. _____ A photograph of John Smith.

7. _____ A map of the Proclamation Line drawn by one of your classmates.

Geography is the study of the Earth. It includes the Earth's land, water, weather, animal life, and plant life. **Geographers** are people who study geography. You can think of yourself as a geographer because you will be learning about places on the Earth.

Location is important to the study of geography. It is almost impossible to figure out your location or find your way around if you do not know the four main, or **cardinal directions.** North, south, east, and west are the **cardinal directions**. On a map these directions are labeled N, S, E, and W.

COMPASS ROSE

Between the four main directions are the **intermediate directions.** Northeast, or NE, is the direction between north and east. Southeast, or SE, is the direction between south and east. Southwest, or SW, is the direction between south and west. Northwest, or NW, is the direction between north and west.

A **reference point** is also important for finding your location. A **reference point** is simply a starting point. It's difficult, for example, to travel southwest if you don't have a starting point.

Example: The Battle of Fort Niagara was one of the final battles of the French and Indian War. In July 1759, the British attacked Fort Niagara with a force of 2,500 men. After 20 days, the French were forced to surrender Fort Niagara to the British. Fort Niagara is located <u>southwest</u> of <u>Lake Ontario</u>.

This example gives you some very important information. It tells you that your **reference point,** or starting point, will be Lake Ontario. Locate Lake Ontario on your French and Indian War map. Put your finger on Lake Ontario and slide it <u>southwest</u>. You should see a picture of Fort Niagara already placed there for you.

Sometimes directions contain more than one **reference point**. Look at the example below:

Example: On June 7, 1755, General Edward Braddock marched 1,000 of his British soldiers toward Fort Duquesne (do•CANE). When Braddock and his men stopped to rest, 300 French soldiers and their Native American allies jumped from behind trees and attacked Braddock's large army. General Braddock was killed in what became known as the Battle of the Wilderness. The Battle of the Wilderness was fought <u>west</u> of <u>Harrisburg</u> and <u>southeast</u> of <u>Fort Niagara</u>.

This example contains two **reference points** and two sets of directions. They have been underlined for you. Look at your French and Indian War map. Put your finger on Harrisburg and slide it <u>west</u>. Since there are two battle sites located west, a second **reference point** has been added to help you find your location.

The second **reference point** is Fort Niagara. Place your finger on Fort Niagara and slide it <u>southeast</u>. By using both of these **reference points**, you should be able to easily locate the Battle of the Wilderness.

Directions: In this activity you will use reference points, cardinal directions, and intermediate directions to plot important French and Indian War battle sites on a map. Many of these points of interest **preserve** history. This helps historians learn more about the people who lived before us.

1.   Use your scissors to carefully cut out the symbols on the bottom of the last page.

2.   Label the cardinal and intermediate directions on the compass rose drawn for you on the blank French and Indian War map.

3.   Use the written directions and your compass rose to correctly locate these battles on your French and Indian War map.

4.   To get you started, the reference points and directions have been underlined for you in the first five descriptions. You may want to underline the reference points and directions in the rest of the activity.

5.   Glue the symbols in their proper places on your map. (Glue the symbols right over the dots.)

6.   When you have finished, ask your teacher to pull down the classroom map of the world. Neatly label each state and Canadian **province** with its correct name. Use your coloring pencils to add color to your French and Indian War map.

1.   On July 3, 1754, the Battle of Great Meadows marked the first major battle of the French and Indian War. More than 1,000 French soldiers attacked 21 year old George Washington and his small army at Fort Necessity. Washington and his men fought back, but they were unable to **defeat** the huge army of French soldiers. After losing 100 men, Washington surrendered Fort Necessity to the French. The Battle of Great Meadows was fought <u>west</u> of the <u>Battle of the Wilderness</u>.

2.   The Battle of Lake George was fought on September 8, 1755. During the battle, 1,500 French and Native American troops were defeated by more than 1,000 colonists and 200 of their Native American allies from the Mohawk tribe. The Battle of Lake George was fought <u>southwest</u> of <u>Montpelier</u> and <u>north</u> of <u>Albany</u>.

3.   On March 27, 1756, the French attacked the British at Fort Bull. The battle, which was won by the French, left 76 British soldiers and one French soldier dead. Thirty five British soldiers were taken as prisoners before Fort Bull was burned to the ground. Fort Bull is located <u>northwest</u> of <u>Albany</u> and <u>east</u> of <u>Fort Niagara</u>.

4.   On August 10, 1756, French soldiers from Canada captured and took control of Fort Oswego. In addition to 1,700 prisoners, the French also **seized** 121 British cannons. Capturing Fort Oswego also gave the French control of Lake Ontario. Fort Oswego is located <u>northwest</u> of <u>Fort Bull</u> and <u>southeast</u> of <u>Lake Ontario</u>.

5.   The Battle of Bloody Creek was fought on December 8, 1757. While chopping wood, British soldiers were **ambushed** by a Native American force. One British soldier was killed and seven were taken as **captives** during the short battle. The Battle of Bloody Creek was fought <u>southwest</u> of <u>Halifax</u>.

6.   The Battle of Fort Frontenac took place from August 25 to August 27, 1758. Fort Frontenac was a French fort and trading post. British troops ambushed the fort, trapping 110 French soldiers inside. After two days, the French surrendered Fort Frontenac and all of its supplies to the British. Fort Frontenac is located southeast of Toronto and north of Fort Oswego.

7.   On June 27, 1759, British forces led by Jeffrey Amherst marched toward French controlled Fort Carillon. Along the way, Amherst and his men cut off supply lines to the fort. The French quickly surrendered and the British easily took control of Fort Carillon. Fort Carillon is located southwest of Montpelier and east of Fort Frontenac.

8. The Battle of the Plains of Abraham began on September 12, 1759. The battle involved less than 10,000 troops between the British and French, but it was an important battle in deciding which country would take control of **New France**. During the one hour battle, each side lost more than 600 men. The British Army and British Navy successfully defeated the French Army. The Battle of the Plains of Abraham was fought northeast of Québec City and northwest of Augusta.

9. On September 15, 1762, the Battle of Signal Hill was the final land battle of the French and Indian War. British troops climbed the hill controlled by the French. In a surprise attack, the French commander was seriously wounded. When the battle ended, Signal Hill was in the hands of the British. The Battle of Signal Hill was fought north of St. John's.

10. The Battle of Restigouche was a naval battle fought between the British Royal Navy and the French Navy in the spring of 1760. The French ships, loaded with supplies and troops, were blocked by British ships. The British victory at Restigouche made the French realize that they had no chance of holding onto its land in North America. The Battle of Restigouche was fought northeast of Fredericton.

Battle of Great Meadows

Battle of Lake George

Fort Bull

Fort Oswego

Battle of Bloody Creek

Fort Frontenac

Fort Carillon

Battle of Plains of Abraham

Battle of Signal Hill

Battle of Restigouche

Name _____

French and Indian War Map

St. John's

Halifax

Fredericton

Augusta

Québec City

Montpelier

Concord

Albany

Toronto

Harrisburg

Lake Ontario

Lake Erie

Fort Niagara

Battle of the Wilderness

Compass Rose

Canada

English Colonies

Early American Government © 2009
splashpublications.com

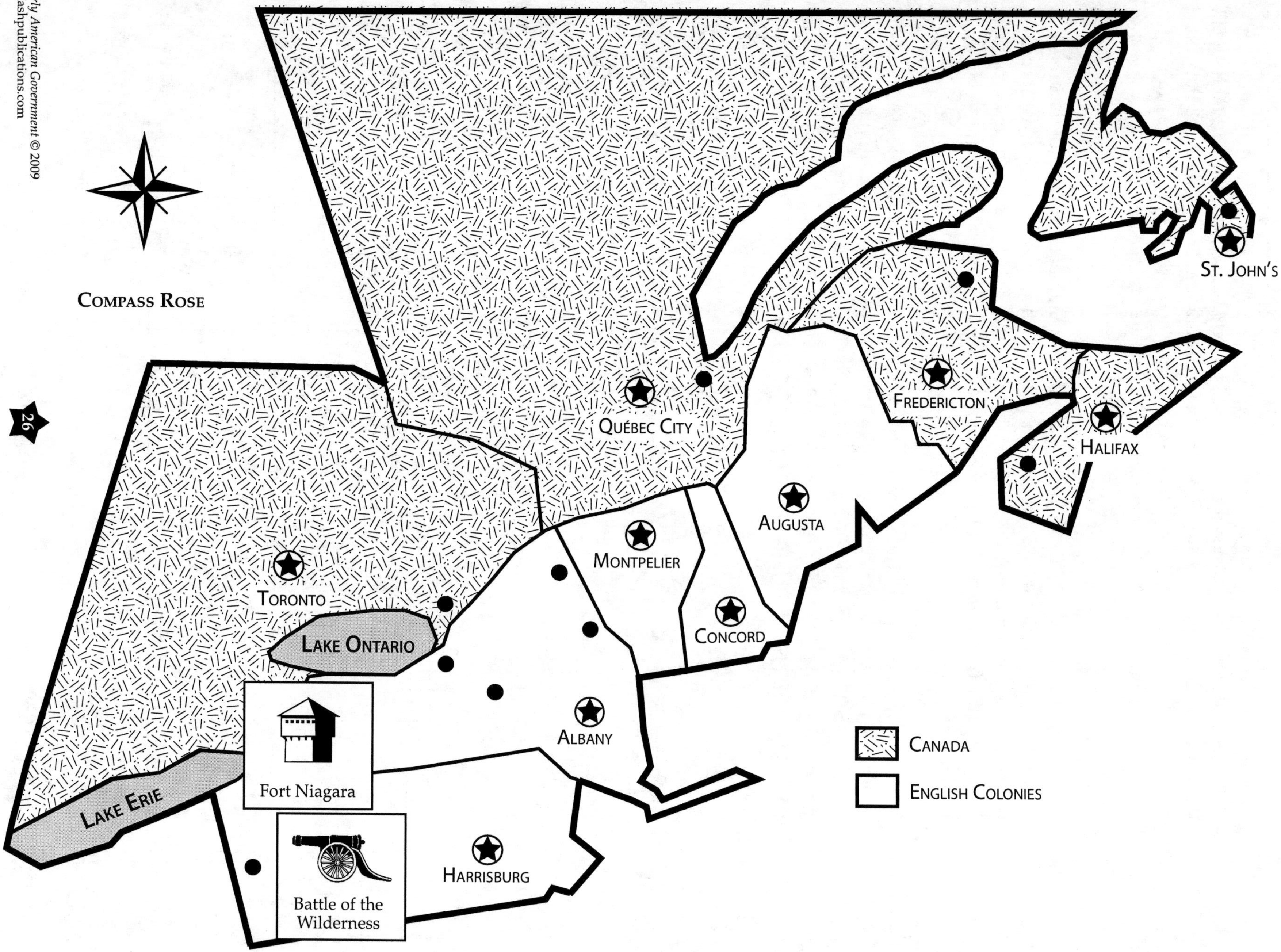

Name _____

 **VOCABULARY QUIZ**

EARLY AMERICAN GOVERNMENT
PART III

Directions: Match the vocabulary word on the left with its definition on the right. Put the letter for the definition on the blank next to the vocabulary word it matches. Use each word and definition only once.

1. _____ allies

2. _____ surrendered

3. _____ ambushed

4. _____ seized

5. _____ autobiography

6. _____ sawmills

7. _____ resources

8. _____ captives

9. _____ reserved

10. _____ defeat

11. _____ raided

12. _____ European

13. _____ profit

A. a part of a country having a government of its own.

B. took by force.

C. prisoners who have been taken without permission.

D. gave up.

E. money made after all expenses have been paid.

F. to win victory over.

G. French colonies in North America that were given to Great Britain after the French and Indian War.

H. an official announcement.

I. stories of a person's life written by someone else.

J. groups of people who come together to help one another in times of trouble.

K. protect from injury or ruin so more can be learned.

L. entered someone's property to steal from them.

14. _____ Great Lakes

15. _____ gristmills

16. _____ province

17. _____ ignored

18. _____ proclamation

19. _____ indigo

20. _____ preserve

21. _____ biographies

22. _____ New France

23. _____ outraged

M. five large lakes located in North America at the border between Canada and the United States. The names of the lakes are Superior, Michigan, Huron, Erie, and Ontario.

N. a plant which produces a blue dye.

O. the story of your life written by you.

P. a person who comes from the continent of Europe.

Q. didn't listen to.

R. things found in nature that are valuable to humans.

S. mills for grinding grain into flour.

T. businesses with big machines that saw wood into planks and boards.

U. attacked by surprise.

V. angered beyond belief.

W. set aside for a special purpose.

GREAT BRITAIN'S TAXES

By the end of 1763, the English colonists in America realized that Great Britain was in complete control of their lives. The colonists were not permitted to explore or settle the new land that they had fought for during the French and Indian War. King George III gave most of the new land to the Native Americans. British soldiers were sent to keep the colonists from crossing the Proclamation Line.

GREAT BRITAIN'S TAXES

Fighting the French and Indian War was very expensive for Great Britain. Sending soldiers and weapons from Great Britain to America was costly. Protecting the colonists from Native American attacks and guarding the Proclamation Line was also expensive. Great Britain felt that the colonists should pay for these things. After all, they were living in America. The citizens of Great Britain didn't want to pay for battles and protection that didn't affect them.

Great Britain chose to tax the colonists to pay for these things. In April 1764, the Sugar Act placed a tax on **imported** items like sugar, molasses, and wine.

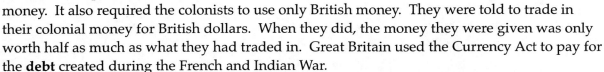

In September 1764, the Currency Act **prohibited** the colonies from printing their own money. It also required the colonists to use only British money. They were told to trade in their colonial money for British dollars. When they did, the money they were given was only worth half as much as what they had traded in. Great Britain used the Currency Act to pay for the **debt** created during the French and Indian War.

The Quartering Act was another money saving plan. Beginning in March 1765, the colonists were required to help pay part of the expenses when British soldiers were in their colonies. The colonists were ordered to supply British soldiers with a place to stay, fuel, candles, and plenty of food to eat.

Beginning in November 1765, the Stamp Act raised money by taxing all kinds of written documents printed in the colonies. This included newspapers, calendars, and legal papers.

THE COLONISTS REVOLT

Once again, the colonists were outraged that Great Britain felt it could tax them whenever and however it wanted. Each colony had established laws that allowed freedom of religion and self government. The colonists felt it was unfair for a country 3,000 miles away to tax them without their permission. The colonists believed that only people they had elected had the power to tax them. They argued that they had not elected any of the leaders in Great Britain.

In December 1765, Virginia became the first colony to take action against what it called "taxation without representation." Led by a lawyer named Patrick Henry, Virginia voted against the Stamp Act. Virginians refused to buy stamps. Other colonies followed Virginia and also stopped buying stamps. They became violent toward the Stamp Masters who were selling the stamps. The colonists destroyed the stamp offices, burned the stamps, and forced the Stamp Masters to leave town. The colonists were successful. In March 1766, the Stamp Act was **repealed**. This was the first time that the American colonists had joined together and **revolted** against Great Britain.

BRITISH SOLDIER

THE TOWNSHEND ACTS

The British government did not like giving in to the disobedient colonists. Great Britain quickly came up with a new plan for raising money. In July 1767, Great Britain passed the Townshend Acts. The Townshend Acts placed a tax on lead, paint, glass, paper, and tea when these items were imported into the colonies. Tax collectors were sent from Great Britain.

The Townshend Acts made the colonists angry. They refused to buy any of Great Britain's products in their stores. This hurt the merchants back in Great Britain because the colonists weren't buying any of their imported items.

THE BOSTON MASSACRE

In March 1770, British troops were sent to Boston to keep peace. The colonists in Boston were not pleased that soldiers had been sent to calm them down. The British soldiers wore red coats as part of their uniforms. The colonists made fun of the soldiers by calling them "Redcoats" or "Lobsterbacks." They threw rocks and eggs at the soldiers. The soldiers fired their guns into the crowd. Five colonists were killed. They were the first colonists to lose their lives in **protest** against Great Britain's rules. The killing of the five colonists became known as the Boston Massacre. After the Boston Massacre, Great Britain removed the soldiers from Boston. In April 1770, Great Britain also ended most of the Townshend Acts. The tax on tea remained in effect.

THE BOSTON TEA PARTY

The colonists responded to the tea tax by **boycotting** British tea. Great Britain even tried to trick the colonists into buying tea by lowering the price on it. On December 6, 1773, three ships entered the Boston Harbor. They were loaded with British tea. A group of colonists, led by Samuel Adams, **disguised** themselves as Native Americans. They raided the ships and dumped 342 chests of tea into the Boston Harbor. The event, known as the Boston Tea Party, angered King George III. He immediately passed laws to punish the colonists for the Boston Tea Party.

THE INTOLERABLE ACTS

The new laws passed by the British government became known as the **Intolerable** Acts. Beginning in March 1774, the Boston Harbor was closed until the colonists paid for the lost tea and showed proper respect to Great Britain's authority. Another law prohibited the colonies from making their own rules and laws. The British soldiers were sent back to Boston. The colonists were again required to provide food and housing to the soldiers.

The Intolerable Acts created even more **hostility** and anger towards Great Britain. The colonists refused to give in to these demands. They had risked everything to come to America where they could live freely. Now they faced the possibility of being ruled by a country that was 3,000 miles away.

FAST FACTS

★ There were actually four ships sent to deliver tea in the Boston Harbor. The fourth ship never made it. It was damaged in a storm and had to come ashore at Cape Cod.
★ Most people think that the Boston Tea Party ships belonged to the British. They were actually American ships loaded with British tea.
★ The ships were not destroyed during the Boston Tea Party. In fact, the protesters cleaned the ships and even replaced a lock that had been broken during the raid.

Name _____

Directions: Read each question carefully. Darken the circle for the correct answer.

---

1 **What caused Great Britain to begin taxing the colonists?**

   A Debt from the French and Indian War.

   B The cost of sending soldiers to guard the Proclamation Line.

   C The cost of protecting the colonists from Native American attacks.

   D All of the above.

2 **Which of Great Britain's rules required the colonists to provide housing and food for British soldiers?**

   F The Stamp Act

   G The Quartering Act

   H The Sugar Act

   J The Currency Act

3 **Which of the following placed a tax on imported wine?**

   A The Stamp Act

   B The Quartering Act

   C The Sugar Act

   D The Currency Act

4 **After reading about the Townshend Acts, you can conclude that –**

   F they taxed the colonists for buying stamps

   G they affected the British merchants as much as they affected the colonists

   H they taxed Native American items like blankets and jewelry

   J the colonists were happy to pay the tax on imported items like paper and paint

5 **What can you learn from reading about the Boston Massacre?**

   A Five colonists were killed.

   B Five British soldiers were killed.

   C The soldiers threw eggs at the colonists.

   D The soldiers made fun of the colonists and called them names.

6 **The colonists responded to the tea tax by boycotting British tea. <u>Boycotting</u> means about the same thing as –**

   F throwing

   G buying

   H refusing

   J selling

7 **Why did the colonists dump the chests of tea into the Boston Harbor?**

   A They hated tea.

   B They wanted to show Great Britain how angry they were.

   C They had so much tea that they could afford to waste a few barrels.

   D They didn't want the Native Americans to get any of the tea.

READING

Answers

1 Ⓐ Ⓑ Ⓒ Ⓓ   5 Ⓐ Ⓑ Ⓒ Ⓓ

2 Ⓕ Ⓖ Ⓗ Ⓙ   6 Ⓕ Ⓖ Ⓗ Ⓙ

3 Ⓐ Ⓑ Ⓒ Ⓓ   7 Ⓐ Ⓑ Ⓒ Ⓓ

4 Ⓕ Ⓖ Ⓗ Ⓙ

Name _____

 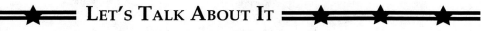

GREAT BRITAIN'S TAXES

During the 1760s, Great Britain raised money by taxing the colonists. This made the colonists very angry. Read the questions below about Great Britain's taxes. Write your answers on the lines provided. Attach a separate piece of paper if you need more room. Be ready to discuss some of your answers.

• **The Stamp Act, the Sugar Act, the Quartering Act, and the Currency Act were all part of Great Britain's plan to raise money.**

If you had been a colonist during the 1760s, which of the above "acts" would have angered you the most? Give reasons for your answer.

_____

_____

_____

Explain, in your own words, what is meant by "taxation without representation."

_____

_____

_____

• **During the Boston Tea Party, colonists disguised themselves as Native Americans and dumped 342 chests of tea into the Boston Harbor.**

When you are angry about something, what do you do to express your anger? Do you agree with the way the colonists expressed their anger?

_____

_____

_____

_____

Name _____

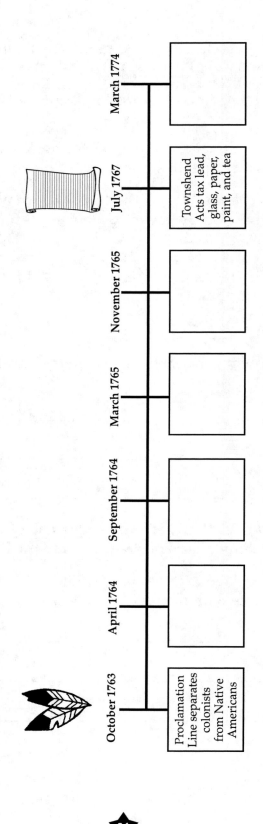

A time line is a tool used to list dates and events in the order that they happened. The time line below lists the important dates of Great Britain's taxes on the colonists. Notice that many of the events are missing.

October 1763	April 1764	September 1764	March 1765	November 1765	July 1767	March 1774
Proclamation Line separates colonists from Native Americans					Townshend Acts tax lead, glass, paper, paint, and tea	

PART I

Directions: In the first part of this activity, you will use your information about Great Britain's taxes to fill in the missing events on the time line. Then, choose the picture that you think best represents each event. Color and cut out each picture before gluing it into its proper spot on the time line. Since you were not present for any of these events, this time line would be a **secondary source**.

Stamp Act taxes all written documents	Intolerable Acts punish colonists and close Boston Harbor	Currency Act prohibits colonies from printing money	Sugar Act taxes imported sugar, wine and molasses	Quartering Act requires colonists to house and feed soldiers

Early American Government © 2009
splashpublications.com

34

Name _____

PART II

Directions: In the second part of this activity, you will create a time line of the five other events that you just read about during the 1760s and 1770s. Again, since you weren't there for any of these events, this time line would be considered a **secondary source**.

1. Use the boxes drawn and your information about Great Britain's Taxes to make a time line of the following events: The Boston Massacre, the repealing of the Stamp Act, Virginia's action against "Taxation without Representation," The Boston Tea Party, and the end of the Townshend Acts.

2. Put the month and year in the top boxes and the events in the bottom boxes. Make sure the dates are in order!

3. Above each date, draw a picture to represent the event.

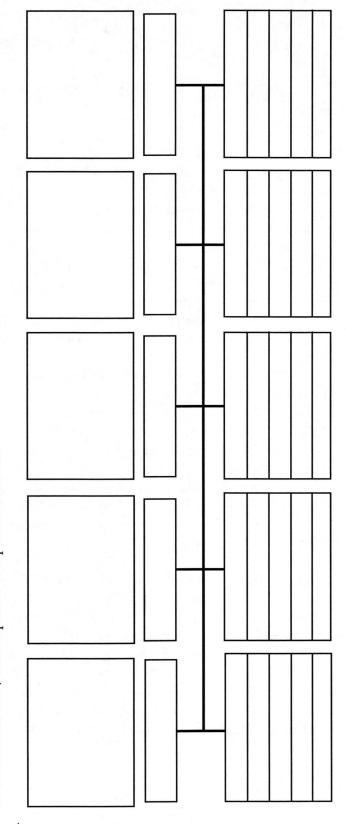

Early American Government © 2009
splashpublications.com

THE CONTINENTAL CONGRESS

During the ten year period between 1763 and 1773, the colonists in America had been punished by Great Britain's Proclamation Line, unfair taxes, and unwanted soldiers. In 1774, Great Britain closed the Boston Harbor. The colonists were afraid that if they didn't do something soon, Great Britain would take complete control of their lives forever.

THE FIRST CONTINENTAL CONGRESS

On September 5, 1774, twelve of the thirteen colonies sent representatives to the First Continental Congress. The meeting was held at Carpenter's Hall in Philadelphia. The colonists needed to decide what to do about Great Britain's cruel treatment. The leaders of the meeting included Samuel Adams, Patrick Henry, and future presidents George Washington and John Adams.

The representatives were all in agreement that Great Britain's taxes and treatment were unfair. They were not in agreement about what to do. Pennsylvania and New York sent **delegates** to find a solution to the problems and make peace with Great Britain. Georgia didn't even send a representative. It was under constant attack by Native Americans and needed the help of British soldiers. The rest of the delegates were split between finding a solution and separating from Great Britain.

In the end, the representatives voted to end all trade with Great Britain until the Intolerable Acts were repealed. They wrote letters to King George III, asking him to **abolish** the Intolerable Acts. The representatives of the First Continental Congress told the colonists to begin training for war.

THE BEGINNING OF THE REVOLUTIONARY WAR

On April 18, 1775, The first shots of the **Revolutionary War** were fired in Lexington, Massachusetts. British troops dressed in bright red uniforms had marched toward the towns of Lexington and Concord searching for the colonists' hidden weapons and gunpowder. Fortunately, the **minutemen** had been warned by Paul Revere that the British were coming. In a quick battle, three Redcoats and two minutemen were killed.

The British soldiers turned back toward Boston. Along the 16 mile journey, more minutemen fired at them from behind trees and stone fences. Over 200 British Redcoats and 90 American minutemen were wounded or killed during the battle.

THE SECOND CONTINENTAL CONGRESS

After the battles of Lexington and Concord, the colonists knew they needed to get organized to have any chance of defeating Great Britain. On May 10, 1775, delegates of the Second Continental Congress met at the State House in Philadelphia. Sixty five representatives from each of the thirteen original colonies gathered to take control of the war. New delegates included John Hancock, Benjamin Franklin, and future president Thomas Jefferson.

Representative John Adams wanted to organize a **Continental Army** with troops from each of the thirteen colonies. The Congress asked George Washington to be the commander of the Continental Army. He accepted the job.

PATRIOTS AND LOYALISTS

General Washington had a difficult job facing him. He traveled to Boston and took charge of the military camps. He found that the **militia** (muh•LIH•shuh) was poorly trained. They didn't have any weapons. The training camps were dirty. If the colonists were going to win this war, they would need money, supplies, and training. Most importantly, the Continental Army needed **loyalty**.

Loyalty proved to be a big problem for General Washington and his Continental Army. Some of the colonists called themselves **Patriots**. The Patriots were willing to support the fight against Great Britain. They volunteered to fight and helped raise money for the war.

Some of the colonists were Loyalists. The Loyalists still supported Great Britain. The Loyalists fought in the British Army, spied on American soldiers, and burned the homes and farms of Patriots.

AMERICAN PATRIOT

There were also colonists who didn't take either side and refused to fight at all. General Washington worked hard to pull his army together so they would be ready for battle.

Name _____

Directions: Read each question carefully. Darken the circle for the correct answer.

---

1 Which colony did not send a representative to the First Continental Congress?

A New York

B Delaware

C Georgia

D Pennsylvania

2 What was this colony's reason for not attending the meeting?

F It didn't think there was anything wrong with the way the colonists were being treated.

G It was too far to travel.

H It couldn't decide who to send.

J It was having difficulty with Native Americans and needed Great Britain's help.

3 In which colony were the first shots of the Revolutionary War fired?

A Massachusetts

B Pennsylvania

C New York

D North Carolina

4 About how much time passed between the First Continental Congress and the Second Continental Congress?

F Less than a month

G More than a year

H Less than a year

J Less than a week

5 Who was asked to be in charge of the Continental Army?

A Benjamin Franklin

B Thomas Jefferson

C George Washington

D John Adams

6 When the commander of the Continental Army visited the military camps in Boston, he found that –

F the soldiers were well trained

G the soldiers had plenty of weapons

H he would need to find a way to spend all of the money that had been given to him to train the soldiers

J the soldiers were poorly trained

7 If you had been a Patriot, you <u>probably</u> would have –

A fought for Great Britain

B fought in the Continental Army

C refused to fight

D fought in the British Army

READING

Answers

1 Ⓐ Ⓑ Ⓒ Ⓓ   5 Ⓐ Ⓑ Ⓒ Ⓓ

2 Ⓕ Ⓖ Ⓗ Ⓙ   6 Ⓕ Ⓖ Ⓗ Ⓙ

3 Ⓐ Ⓑ Ⓒ Ⓓ   7 Ⓐ Ⓑ Ⓒ Ⓓ

4 Ⓕ Ⓖ Ⓗ Ⓙ

LET'S TALK ABOUT IT

THE CONTINENTAL CONGRESS

The Continental Congress met twice to discuss how to handle Great Britain's unfair treatment of the colonists. Read the questions below about the Continental Congress. Write your answers on the lines provided. Attach a separate piece of paper if you need more room. Be ready to discuss some of your answers.

• **During the First Continental Congress, the representatives weren't sure that they wanted to take action against Great Britain.**

If you had been a representative of the First Continental Congress, would you have voted to go to war against Great Britain or try to work out a peaceful agreement? Give reasons for your answer.

_____

_____

_____

_____

• **Loyalty proved to be the biggest problem facing General George Washington and his Continental Army.**

In your opinion, what's worse: someone who fights against you or someone who refuses to choose a side? Explain.

_____

_____

_____

_____

In your own words, describe the difference between a Patriot and a Loyalist.

Patriot: _____

Loyalist: _____

In 1774, representatives from twelve of the thirteen original colonies met in Philadelphia at Carpenter's Hall. After the historic meeting, the representatives told the colonists to prepare for war with Great Britain. Seven months later, the first shots of the Revolutionary War were fired. Today, Carpenter's Hall still stands in Philadelphia. It is part of the Independence National Historic Park.

In this activity, you will follow written directions to make a model of Carpenter's Hall.

1. Cut out the Front and Back Carpenter's Hall patterns and fold as shown.

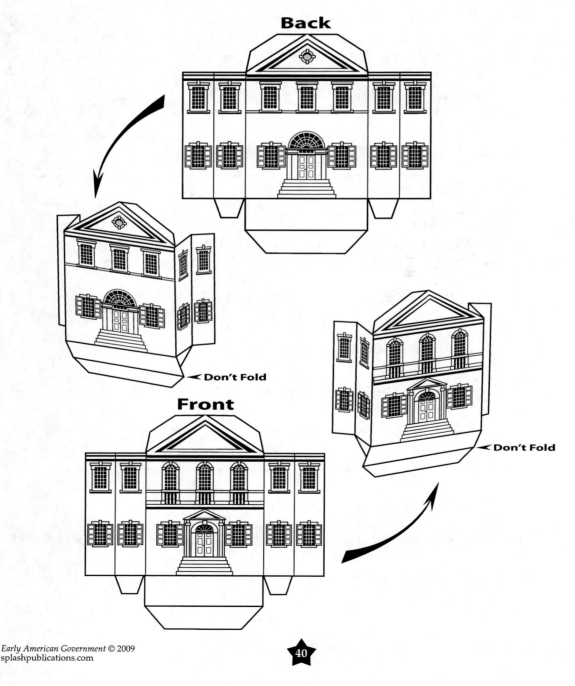

2. As shown below, fold and glue down A Tabs on both the Front and Back Carpenter's Hall patterns.

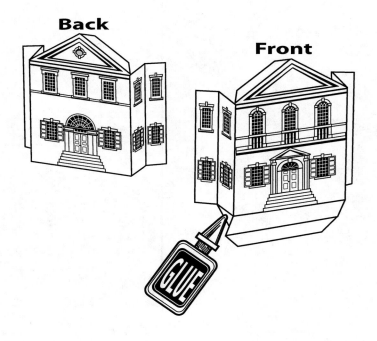

3. Cut out the Front and Back roof patterns. Fold under and glue B Tab to the underside of each roof.

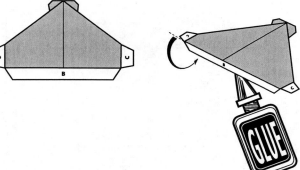

4. Fold each of the two roof patterns as shown below.

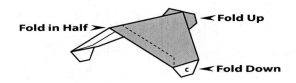

5. As shown below, use glue to attach one roof on the front of Carpenter's Hall. Glue the other roof to the back of Carpenter's Hall. Set the front and back pieces aside for later.

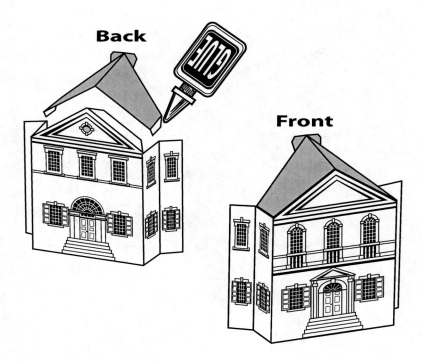

6. Cut out Side 1 and fold as shown below.

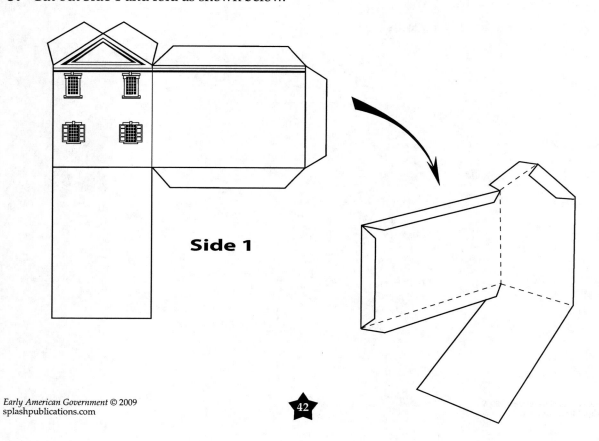

Side 1

7. Cut out Side 2 and fold as shown below.

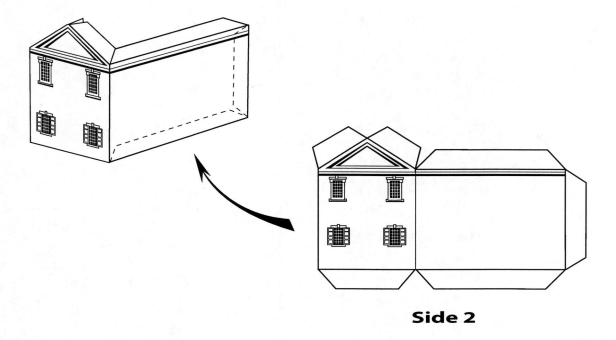

Side 2

8. Glue Side 1 to Side 2. **Do not glue the floor yet.**

9. Cut out Side Roof.

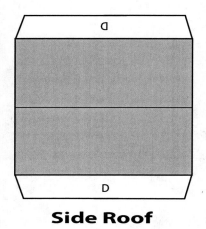

Side Roof

10. Fold both D Tabs under and glue.

11. Fold Side Roof in half as shown below.

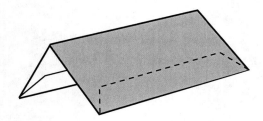

12. Glue Side Roof on top of Carpenter's Hall as shown below.
(HINT: push your hand up through the open floor to help you attach the Roof.)

13. Glue the floor to the bottom of Carpenter's Hall as shown below.

14. Glue the Front and Back of Carpenter's Hall to the Sides as shown below. (The Tabs that stick out on the bottom should be glued to the bottom of the floor.)

15. Cut out the Tower Base. (Don't forget to cut on the dotted lines, too!)

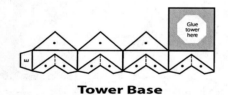

Tower Base

16. Fold all of the Tabs with dots under. Fold solid black lines into a square as shown below.

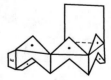

17. Complete the square by gluing Tab E to the opposite side.

18. As a final step, glue the top of the square to the triangle-shaped tabs.

19. Cut out the Tower.

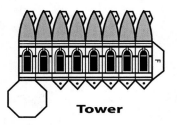

Tower

20. Fold Tab F and glue it to the opposite side as shown. **Do not fold the triangle-shaped tabs.**

21. Glue flag-shaped tabs to one another to form Dome. (HINT: push your finger into the bottom of the Dome for support while you glue.)

22. Glue bottom of Dome to triangle-shaped tabs. Allow Dome to dry before going to the next step.

23. Glue Dome to the Tower Base.

24. Glue Dome on top of Carpenter's Hall as shown below.

★ ★ ★ ★ FAST FACTS ★ ★ ★ ★

★ Carpenter's Hall was built in 1724 by Robert Smith of the Carpenters' Company. Smith built Carpenter's Hall as a place where **architects**, builders, and craftsmen could gather to share ideas about the art of building.

★ Carpenter's Hall was chosen as the meeting place for the First Continental Congress because the representatives wanted to keep the meeting private. The State House, where most important meetings were held, was full of Loyalists who might overhear the colonists planning for war.

★ During the Revolutionary War, Carpenter's Hall was used as a hospital and to store weapons for the colonists fighting against Great Britain.

★ Today, visitors to Carpenter Hall will find eight of the actual chairs used by members of the First Continental Congress.

CARPENTER'S HALL PATTERNS

Front

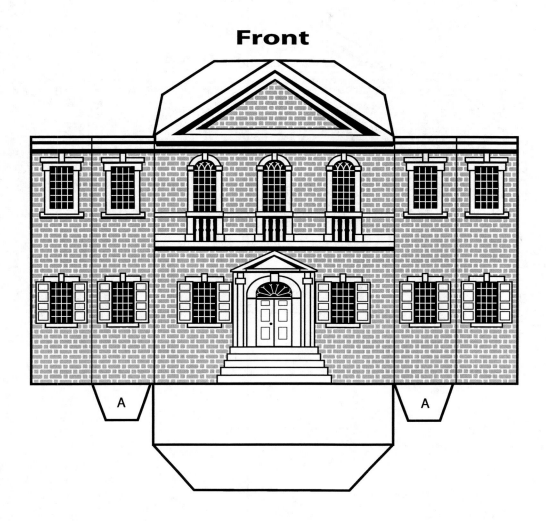

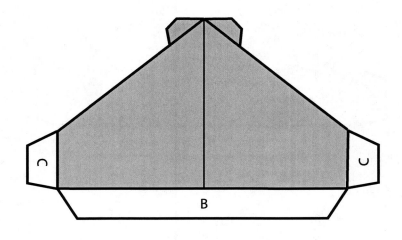

Back

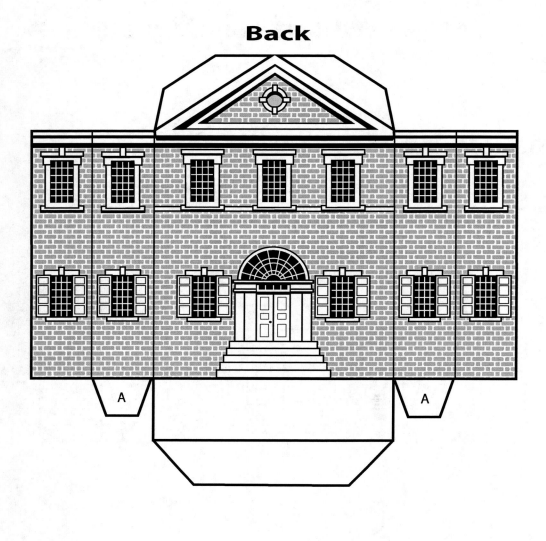

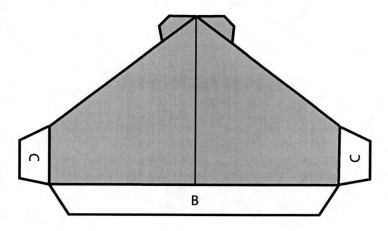

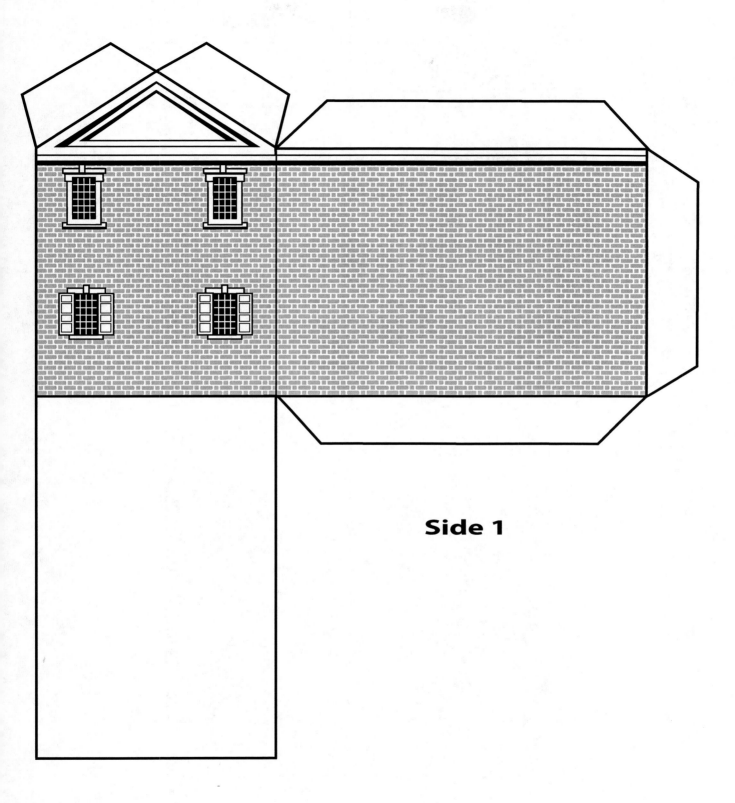

Side 1

Side 2

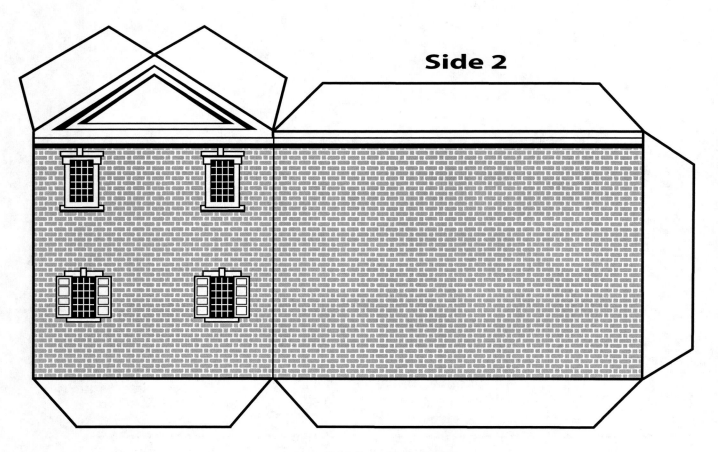

Side Roof

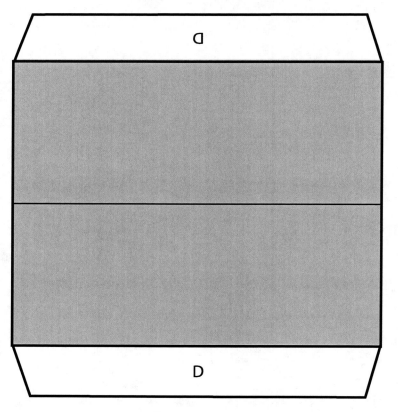

D

D

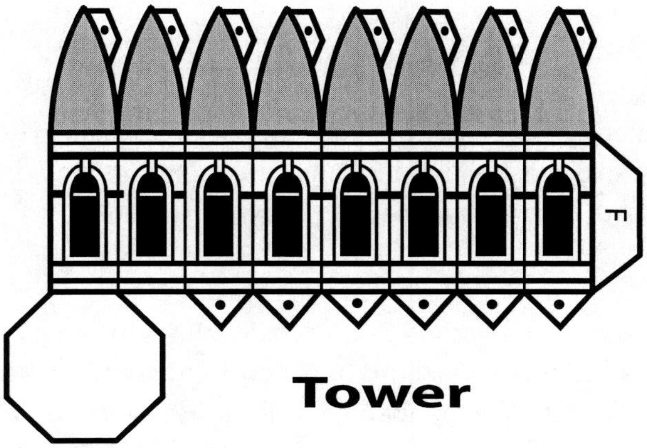

Tower

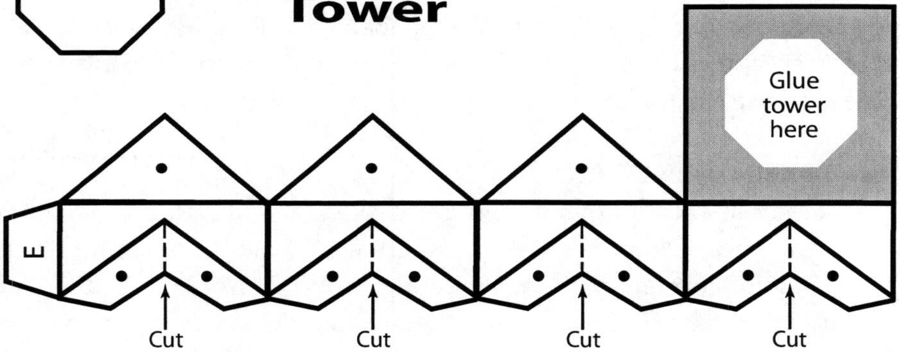

Tower Base

Glue tower here

E

F

Cut   Cut   Cut   Cut

THE DECLARATION OF INDEPENDENCE

By the winter of 1775, the colonists had battled Great Britain for almost a year. The delegates of the Second Continental Congress believed that the colonies should declare their independence from Great Britain. Many colonists were not ready to hear this.

THOMAS PAINE

In January 1776, a man by the name of Thomas Paine wrote a book titled *Common Sense*. In his book, Mr. Paine wrote that it was silly for an island 3,000 miles away to make the rules in America. He also wrote that King George III was not a friendly king trying to help the colonists. Over 100,000 copies of Thomas Paine's book sold in just three months. His ideas made sense to the colonists. They were finally ready for a change.

THOMAS JEFFERSON'S DOCUMENT

In June 1776, the Second Continental Congress set up a committee of five men to write a statement of independence. The committee members were John Adams, Thomas Jefferson, Benjamin Franklin, Roger Sherman, and Robert Livingston. Thomas Jefferson was chosen to write the document. Two weeks later, Jefferson had finished the statement of independence.

On July 2, 1776, the Second Continental Congress met to **debate** Jefferson's document. Jefferson accused King George III of taking away the rights of Americans. Jefferson also attacked slavery and the slave trade. The representatives from the Southern colonies owned slaves. They refused to **adopt** Jefferson's statement of independence unless the part about slavery was removed. After many hours of arguing, it was agreed that slavery would not be mentioned in the declaration.

★ ★ ★ FAST FACTS ★ ★ ★

★ Slavery had been a part of the colonies since the early 1500s. Black men, women, and children were captured in western Africa by slave traders and brought to the New World where they were forced into a life of slavery.

★ Slave traders **transported** the slaves across the Atlantic Ocean by ship. Knowing that many would die during the **voyage**, the slave traders packed as many slaves as they could below the decks of the ships. The black captives were chained together and stacked on top of each other.

★ In the New World, slaves were purchased at an auction. White bidders shouted out the price they wanted to pay for a slave. The highest bidder won. The bid for a strong, skilled slave could reach as high as $1,000. This is about $30,000 in today's prices.

THE DECLARATION OF INDEPENDENCE

On July 4, 1776, the Declaration of Independence was adopted. The official document was signed on August 2, 1776, by 56 members of the Second Continental Congress. Signing the Declaration of Independence did not make the American colonists free. It only stated that they deserved to be free and were willing to fight for their freedom.

THOMAS JEFFERSON

The men who signed the Declaration of Independence took a big risk. If America lost the Revolutionary War to Great Britain, the signers would be seen as **traitors**. Under Great Britain's laws, traitors were put to death.

MORE THAN INDEPENDENCE

The Declaration of Independence was more than just a simple statement of independence. There were two very important parts of the declaration that helped shape the United States and other democracies like it.

The first important part of the Declaration of Independence was that government existed for the benefit of the people. If a government, like Great Britain, used its power unfairly, the citizens of the country had a right to **rebel** against and even **overturn** the government.

The second important part of the Declaration of Independence was that all men were created equal. This meant that all citizens deserved protection. Everyone had the right to participate in choosing government leaders and help make decisions that affected them.

The signers of the Declaration of Independence didn't realize it at the time, but their statement about all "men being created equal" would someday give equal rights to all people, including women, blacks, and Native Americans.

THE UNITED STATES OF AMERICA

After signing the Declaration of Independence, the thirteen original colonies joined together. They formed the United States of America. The Declaration of Independence did not end the Revolutionary War. It did let Great Britain know that the United States was prepared to battle for its freedom. The Revolutionary War was far from over.

Name _____

Directions: Read each question carefully. Darken the circle for the correct answer.

1   **What did the delegates of the Second Continental Congress want to do?**

A   Declare their independence from Great Britain.

B   Make peace with Great Britain.

C   Find a way to end the fighting.

D   Split the colonies in half between Patriots and Loyalists.

2   **Who convinced the colonists to follow the advice of the Second Continental Congress?**

F   Thomas Jefferson

G   Benjamin Franklin

H   Thomas Paine

J   George Washington

3   **All of these men were selected to write a statement of independence <u>except</u> –**

A   Benjamin Franklin

B   John Adams

C   Thomas Jefferson

D   George Washington

4   **What had to be removed from the Declaration of Independence before it could be adopted?**

F   Thomas Jefferson's signature.

G   The part about slavery.

H   Rules for voting.

J   Benjamin Franklin's name.

5   **Which of the following is an example of a Primary Source?**

A   A book written in 2005 about the Declaration of Independence.

B   Thomas Jefferson's biography.

C   The original copy of Thomas Paine's book *Common Sense*.

D   A picture of George Washington painted by one of your classmates.

6   **When the signers of the Declaration of Independence signed their names to the document, they were risking their –**

F   money

G   lives

H   jobs

J   friendships

7   **After signing the Declaration of Independence, the thirteen original colonies became –**

A   citizens of Great Britain

B   the United States of America

C   the United Kingdom

D   Patriots

READING

Answers

1   Ⓐ Ⓑ Ⓒ Ⓓ   5   Ⓐ Ⓑ Ⓒ Ⓓ
2   Ⓕ Ⓖ Ⓗ Ⓙ   6   Ⓕ Ⓖ Ⓗ Ⓙ
3   Ⓐ Ⓑ Ⓒ Ⓓ   7   Ⓐ Ⓑ Ⓒ Ⓓ
4   Ⓕ Ⓖ Ⓗ Ⓙ

 **LET'S TALK ABOUT IT**

THE DECLARATION OF INDEPENDENCE

On July 4, 1776, the Declaration of Independence was adopted. Read the questions below about the Declaration of Independence. Write your answers on the lines provided. Attach a separate piece of paper if you need more room. Be ready to discuss some of your answers.

- **July 4th is a national holiday in the United States. Businesses, banks, and post offices are closed on July 4th.**

    The Declaration of Independence was adopted more than two hundred years ago. Do you still think it is necessary for us to celebrate July 4th? Explain why you feel this way.

    _____

    _____

    _____

    _____

- **The signers of the Declaration of Independence would not adopt the document until the part about slavery was removed.**

    If you could have asked the signers of the Declaration of Independence one question about slavery, what would you have asked them?

    _____

    _____

    _____

    How do you think they would have answered your question?

    _____

    _____

    _____

    _____

THE ARTICLES OF CONFEDERATION

In 1776, the Second Continental Congress met and wrote the Declaration of Independence. After its adoption, the thirteen original colonies formed the United States of America. The delegates had to decide who would have power in the United States. The plan adopted by the delegates of the Second Continental Congress was known as the Articles of Confederation.

DIVIDING THE POWER

The Articles of Confederation divided the powers of government between the thirteen states and Congress. This was different from Great Britain's way of ruling. In Great Britain, one group of people had all of the power. The Articles of Confederation put Congress in charge of the United States. The Articles also allowed the individual states to have power over themselves.

Congress was responsible for declaring war, keeping peace, maintaining the Army and Navy, establishing boundaries between states, and setting up a national post office for delivering mail. Each of the thirteen states was expected to cooperate with Congress by taxing its citizens to raise money for war and sending soldiers for the Army and Navy. Each state was also responsible for making its own laws. Congress could not **interfere** with those laws or make decisions for the states.

Each of the thirteen states had one vote in Congress, no matter how big or small the state was. Together, these thirteen voters were known as the Confederation. The Articles of Confederation could only be changed with a unanimous vote of the Confederation.

APPROVING THE ARTICLES OF CONFEDERATION

On November 15, 1777, the Articles of Confederation were approved by the thirteen members of Congress. The Articles were sent to the thirteen states for their approval. On March 1, 1781, after many arguments over land boundaries, the Articles of Confederation were finally approved by each of the thirteen states. By this time, Great Britain had surrendered the Revolutionary War to the United States.

PROBLEMS WITH THE ARTICLES OF CONFEDERATION

There were problems with the Articles of Confederation from the very beginning. After the Revolutionary War, Congress needed money from the states to help pay for the war's debt. Congress also needed the states to send men to join the Army and Navy to protect the United States if war broke out again.

Under the Articles of Confederation, the states were responsible for taxing their citizens. The states were expected to send the money to Congress. The states refused to send money or men for the Army and Navy. This left the **federal government** broke and unable to protect itself.

Congress could pass laws, but it could not enforce them. Congress also had no power over foreign trade or trade between the states. The states argued over boundaries, trade, and taxes. Some states even printed their own paper money. Money that was good in one state could not be spent in another state. The Articles of Confederation granted the independence that each state wanted, but Congress had no authority to make the states work together to solve national problems. Changes needed to be made before the United States fell apart.

FAST FACTS

- ★ Just like there were thirteen states, there were thirteen parts or "articles" to the Articles of Confederation.
- ★ Article Eleven invited Canada to join the United States and become the 14th state.
- ★ Maryland was the last of the thirteen original states to approve the Articles of Confederation.
- ★ The Articles of Confederation allowed states to send between two and seven delegates to Congress each year. Still, each state would only have one vote.

Name _____

THE ARTICLES OF CONFEDERATION
★ COMPREHENSION ★

Directions: Read each question carefully. Darken the circle for the correct answer.

1 According to the first paragraph, the Articles of Confederation were adopted –

    A before the Declaration of Independence

    B during the French and Indian War

    C before the United States was formed

    D after the Declaration of Independence

2 The Articles of Confederation provided a written plan for –

    F the treatment of Native Americans

    G the punishment of Great Britain

    H the United States government

    J ending the French and Indian War

3 According to the Articles of Confederation, Congress was responsible for all of the following <u>except</u> –

    A declaring war

    B keeping peace

    C establishing boundaries between states

    D creating laws for states

4 According to the Articles of Confederation, how many votes did each state have in Congress?

    F As many as they wanted

    G Two

    H It depended on the size of the state

    J One

5 Who was responsible for taxing the citizens to raise money for things the country needed?

    A The states

    B Congress

    C The President

    D Great Britain

6 How many votes did it take to make a change to the Articles of Confederation?

    F At least seven

    G Ten

    H Thirteen

    J No changes could be made to the Articles of Confederation.

7 After reading about the problems with the Articles of Confederation, you learn that –

    A the states sent too much money for the Army and Navy

    B thousands of men from each state joined the Army and Navy

    C money that was printed in some states could not be used in other states

    D the Articles of Confederation completely protected the United States and held the nation together

READING

Answers

1 Ⓐ Ⓑ Ⓒ Ⓓ   5 Ⓐ Ⓑ Ⓒ Ⓓ

2 Ⓕ Ⓖ Ⓗ Ⓙ   6 Ⓕ Ⓖ Ⓗ Ⓙ

3 Ⓐ Ⓑ Ⓒ Ⓓ   7 Ⓐ Ⓑ Ⓒ Ⓓ

4 Ⓕ Ⓖ Ⓗ Ⓙ

Name _____

THE ARTICLES OF CONFEDERATION

The Articles of Confederation were adopted by the delegates of the Second Continental Congress. Read the questions below about the Articles of Confederation. Write your answers on the lines provided. Attach a separate piece of paper if you need more room. Be ready to discuss some of your answers.

- **The Articles of Confederation divided the power between the thirteen states and Congress.**

  In your own words, explain what is meant by <u>the Confederation</u>.

  _____

  _____

  The Articles of Confederation could only be changed with a <u>unanimous</u> vote by the Confederation. Explain what <u>unanimous</u> means.

  _____

  _____

- **There were problems with the Articles of Confederation from the very beginning.**

  Use the lines below to describe one problem with the Articles of Confederation.

  _____

  _____

  If you had been a member of Congress, describe what you would have done to solve this problem.

  _____

  _____

  _____

  _____

Name _____

☆ ★ ☆ ★✦ VOCABULARY QUIZ ☆ ★ ☆ ★✦

EARLY AMERICAN GOVERNMENT
PART IV

Directions: Match the vocabulary word on the left with its definition on the right. Put the letter for the definition on the blank next to the vocabulary word it matches. Use each word and definition only once.

1. _____ Continental Army

2. _____ voyage

3. _____ Patriots

4. _____ revolted

5. _____ boycotting

6. _____ abolish

7. _____ adopt

8. _____ traitors

9. _____ minutemen

10. _____ repealed

11. _____ debt

12. _____ delegates

13. _____ interfere

A. journey that is usually made by water.

B. to destroy the power of; to defeat.

C. done away with; removed.

D. anger and unfriendliness.

E. a group of men having some military training who are called upon only in emergencies.

F. refusing to buy.

G. impossible to put up with; unable to bear.

H. battle for independence between the English colonists in America and Great Britain.

I. accept and put into action.

J. not allowed.

K. to become involved when help is not wanted.

L. faithfulness.

M. people who do things to hurt their countries.

14. _____ transported

15. _____ overturn

16. _____ rebel

17. _____ militia

18. _____ loyalty

19. _____ disguised

20. _____ intolerable

21. _____ imported

22. _____ hostility

23. _____ prohibited

24. _____ protest

25. _____ Revolutionary War

26. _____ federal government

27. _____ debate

28. _____ architects

N. groups of armed men who were prepared to fight on a minute's notice during the Revolutionary War.

O. a discussion that gives arguments for and against a subject.

P. moved products or people from one place to another.

Q. types of items brought into a country for the purpose of selling them.

R. stop or put an end to.

S. to argue against something thought to be unfair.

T. people sent with power to represent others.

U. to battle against authority.

V. people who supported the United States during the Revolutionary War.

W. changed appearance to keep from being recognized.

X. battled against rules and laws felt to be unfair.

Y. American troops that fought against Great Britain during the Revolutionary War.

Z. the group of people at the national level elected to set up a system of rules and laws for our country.

AA. money that is owed to someone else.

BB. people who design buildings.

THE UNITED STATES CONSTITUTION

In 1781, the Articles of Confederation were approved. The Articles served as the first written plan of government for the United States of America. They granted independence to each state. They limited the power of the federal government. The Articles of Confederation gave the citizens of the United States the freedom that they had fought for during the Revolutionary War. Unfortunately, the federal government was powerless to enforce important laws. The states printed their own money and refused to send men to fight in the Army and Navy. By 1786, James Madison, Alexander Hamilton, and others knew that changes needed to be made.

THE CONSTITUTIONAL CONVENTION

In the summer of 1787, representatives from twelve states attended the Constitutional Convention at the Pennsylvania State House in Philadelphia. They met to make changes to the Articles of Confederation. Rhode Island did not want to make any changes, so it refused to send a representative. There were 55 men in attendance at the convention. Most of the men were lawyers, bankers, wealthy land owners, or men who already had experience in government. Many of the delegates had fought in the Revolutionary War. They included famous men like Alexander Hamilton, James Madison, and George Washington. The oldest delegate, Benjamin Franklin, was 81 years old.

George Washington was elected to lead the Constitutional Convention. He established three rules. The first rule was that each of the twelve states present would have one vote. The second rule stated that it would take at least seven states to agree on something before a change would be made to the Articles of Confederation. The third rule was that everything at the meeting had to be kept secret.

THE FATHER OF THE CONSTITUTION

James Madison came to the Constitutional Convention prepared with a plan for uniting the country. His plan created a strong federal government. He took notes about everything that happened during the Constitutional Convention.

James Madison is often called the "Father of the Constitution." It was his well-written plan that **convinced** the delegates to get rid of the Articles of Confederation. Together they wrote a whole new Constitution for the United States.

JAMES MADISON'S PLAN

JAMES MADISON

Madison's plan divided powers between the federal and state governments. It also separated the federal government into three equal branches, or parts. This was important to the delegates because they still did not want the United States ruled by one group the way Great Britain had ruled the colonies. They also agreed that the federal government had to have more power than it did in the Articles of Confederation.

THREE BRANCHES OF GOVERNMENT

Madison's plan clearly outlined the rules for state and federal governments. All state and federal governments would be divided into three branches. These branches would be known as the legislative, executive, and judicial (joo•DIH•shul) branches.

The legislative branch would be the part of the government that made the laws. Congress would be in charge of the legislative branch. It would be Congress's job to make the laws for the country and raise money for the federal government.

The executive branch would be the branch of the federal government that was in charge of carrying out the laws and running the country. The president would be in charge of the executive branch.

The judicial branch would make sure the laws were followed. The **Supreme Court** would be in charge of the judicial branch.

A SYSTEM OF CHECKS AND BALANCES

Each of the three branches of the federal government would need to use its powers to check and balance the other two branches. Balance in the three branches of government was important so that one branch didn't become too powerful. For example, if the executive branch, run by the president, did something wrong, the judicial branch, run by the Supreme Court, could stop the president. If the president **abused** his power, the judicial branch could even remove the president from office.

Another example of this balance required that all laws passed by the legislative branch be approved by the executive branch. This was important if the legislative branch, run by Congress, passed a law that the executive branch disagreed with. In that case, the president could veto the law and refuse to approve it.

EQUAL REPRESENTATION

The delegates knew it was important to give power to the people of the United States. It was decided that government officials would be elected. The people of each state would elect representatives to Congress. Congress would then make decisions for the state. The question was, how many representatives should each state have in Congress?

Under the old Articles of Confederation, each state only had one representative in Congress. It didn't matter how big the state was, it still only received one representative. Each representative in Congress could cast only one vote for his state. Delegates from the larger states argued that they had more people and raised more money from taxes. The larger states felt they should get more than one person in Congress to represent them. Delegates from the smaller states said it wasn't their fault that their states were small in size. The small states wanted to be represented equally in Congress.

THE GREAT COMPROMISE

The delegates of the convention finally came to an agreement that was known as the Great Compromise. A compromise requires each side to give up something in order to make the other side happy. In the Great Compromise, it was agreed that Congress would be divided into two parts, or houses. In one part of Congress, the House of Representatives, the number of representatives would be based on a state's size. The larger states would have more representatives in the House of Representatives than the smaller states. Representatives to the House would be chosen by the people of their states every two years.

The second house of Congress, the Senate, would have two representatives from each state. It didn't matter how large or small the state was, it still received two representatives in the Senate. Senators would be elected by the people of their states every six years. Before a law could be passed, it would have to be approved by a majority of voters in the House of Representatives <u>and</u> the Senate. This way it would be fair for both the larger states and the smaller states.

SLAVERY COMPROMISES

There were also other compromises that needed to be made in the United States Constitution. Two of these compromises involved slavery. The representatives argued about how slaves should be counted. The Southern states owned the most slaves. They wanted slaves to count as part of their **population**. This would help them get more representatives in the House of Representatives. The Northern states argued that slaves were property, not people. It was finally agreed that five slaves would count for three people.

The other compromise involved importing slaves from Africa. The Northern states wanted slavery ended completely. The Southern states argued that they needed slaves to help them on their farms and **plantations**. Some Southern states wanted to stop importing slaves from Africa. They wanted to raise and sell slaves themselves and make a profit. It was finally agreed that Congress would allow slaves to be imported from Africa until 1808. After that time, it would be **illegal** to bring slaves from Africa into the United States.

A POWERFUL CONGRESS

The writers of the United States Constitution also gave a lot of power to Congress. This was different from the Articles of Confederation where Congress had little power over the states. In the United States Constitution, Congress held the power to control trade within the United States. Congress also controlled the trade between the United States and other countries. Congress could also raise money through taxes and borrow money from the federal government. Congress was also in charge of printing money and deciding on its value. Individual states were no longer permitted to print their own money.

BALANCING THE STATE AND FEDERAL GOVERNMENTS

The final problem faced by the delegates of the Constitutional Convention was how much power to give the federal government. Under Great Britain's rule, the federal government was too powerful. Under the Articles of Confederation, the federal government was too weak. The delegates decided that there needed to be a balance between the federal government and the state governments.

It was decided that the legislative, executive, and judicial branches of the federal government would be in charge of making and enforcing laws that affected the entire nation. This included printing money, controlling trade, declaring war, and keeping peace.

The state governments would have the power to make and enforce laws that affected their states. State laws could not interfere with federal laws. For example, if the federal government declared war and required men to volunteer for the Army and Navy, the state governments could not pass a law that permitted men not to volunteer.

The states could raise taxes to pay for things needed in the state. The states would also be in charge of building public schools. The delegates of the Constitutional Convention knew that it would be very important to make these powers clear in the United States Constitution. This would avoid problems between the federal and state governments.

★==★==★= FAST FACTS =★==★==★

★ In 1808, importing slaves from Africa was **outlawed**. This didn't stop slave traders from importing slaves illegally. The practice of kidnapping slaves from Africa continued well into the 1860s.

★ The president of the United States can only be elected to two terms of office and serve a total of eight years. There is no limit to the number of times senators and representatives can be elected to office.

★ At 81, Benjamin Franklin was the oldest delegate at the Constitutional Convention. Twenty six year old Jonathon Dayton of New Jersey was the youngest delegate.

★ George Washington was unanimously chosen as the president of the Constitutional Convention. He was the only delegate who did not go to college.

THE PREAMBLE (PRE•AM•BUL)

The United States Constitution also included the goals of the United States. These goals were listed in the first part, or the Preamble of the Constitution. The Preamble stated that it was important to establish a strong government that would unite the nation and guarantee peace and **justice**. Other goals listed in the Preamble included defending the nation against enemies, promising the safety and well-being of all people, and making sure that everyone in the nation would always be free.

RATIFYING THE CONSTITUTION

The representatives of the Constitutional Convention worked the entire summer on the United States Constitution. On September 17, 1787, the United States Constitution was signed by 39 members of the Constitutional Congress. It was then sent to the thirteen states for their approval. The rules stated that nine of the thirteen states needed to approve the United States Constitution before it could become law.

On December 7, 1787, Delaware became the first state to **ratify** the Constitution. Pennsylvania and New Jersey followed a week later. By the second week of January 1788, Georgia and Connecticut had joined them. On June 21, 1788, New Hampshire became the ninth state to approve the Constitution. The United States Constitution had enough votes to put it into effect.

By the end of the summer, New York and Virginia had ratified the United States Constitution. It took another year before the last two states, North Carolina and Rhode Island, finally approved the Constitution. All thirteen original states had accepted the "supreme law of the land."

FAST FACTS

★ The United States Constitution was written in the same Pennsylvania State House where the Declaration of Independence was signed and George Washington accepted the job as commander of the Continental Army. Today, the building still stands in Philadelphia, but its name has been changed to Independence Hall.

★ The United States Constitution is four pages long with over 4,000 hand-written words. There are many spelling and grammar mistakes in the hand-written copy of the Constitution.

★ The original copy of the United States Constitution is so valuable, it is stored in a bullet proof case with **helium** and water added to protect the paper. Only pages one and four are on display in Washington, D.C.

★ The words democracy and education are not mentioned in the United States Constitution.

Name _____

THE UNITED STATES CONSTITUTION
★ COMPREHENSION ★

Directions: Read each question carefully. Darken the circle for the correct answer.

1   **Which state did not send a representative to the Constitutional Convention?**

   A   Maryland

   B   Georgia

   C   Rhode Island

   D   Pennsylvania

2   **Which of the following was not one of George Washington's rules for the Constitutional Convention?**

   F   Everything at the meeting must be kept secret.

   G   Each of the twelve states would have one vote.

   H   The delegates were not permitted to leave the room.

   J   At least seven states must agree before a change would be made to the Articles of Confederation.

3   **Who is known as the "Father of the Constitution?"**

   A   Benjamin Franklin

   B   Alexander Hamilton

   C   James Madison

   D   George Washington

4   **All of the following are branches of state and federal governments except –**

   F   judicial

   G   supreme

   H   executive

   J   legislative

5   **Which branch of the government is in charge of making laws?**

   A   judicial

   B   supreme

   C   executive

   D   legislative

6   **After reading about the Great Compromise, you can conclude that –**

   F   slavery was the biggest issue of the Great Compromise

   G   nobody was happy with the Great Compromise

   H   only large states got what they wanted in the Great Compromise

   J   large states and small states had to come to an agreement to get what they wanted

7   **Which of the following is a responsibility of state governments?**

   A   Building public schools.

   B   Declaring war.

   C   Printing money.

   D   Controlling trade.

READING

Answers

1 Ⓐ Ⓑ Ⓒ Ⓓ   5 Ⓐ Ⓑ Ⓒ Ⓓ
2 Ⓕ Ⓖ Ⓗ Ⓙ   6 Ⓕ Ⓖ Ⓗ Ⓙ
3 Ⓐ Ⓑ Ⓒ Ⓓ   7 Ⓐ Ⓑ Ⓒ Ⓓ
4 Ⓕ Ⓖ Ⓗ Ⓙ

Name _____

THE UNITED STATES CONSTITUTION

The United States Constitution replaced the Articles of Confederation as the plan for our nation's government. Read the questions below about the United States Constitution. Write your answers on the lines provided. Attach a separate piece of paper if you need more room. Be ready to discuss some of your answers.

• **James Madison's plan for the United States Government included a system of Checks and Balances.**

   Explain why it is important to have checks and balances in the Constitution.

   _____

   _____

• **Compromises were made in the United States Constitution.**

   What does it mean to compromise?

   _____

   _____

   Describe one <u>slavery compromise</u> made in the Constitution. Do you think this compromise was important? Explain.

   _____

   _____

   _____

   Describe the last time that you had to compromise. Explain why it was important for you to compromise.

   _____

   _____

   _____

   _____

GEORGE WASHINGTON

George Washington was born on February 22, 1732. He was the oldest son of Augustine Washington and his second wife Mary Ball Washington. Augustine was a wealthy plantation owner who also found time to teach young George at home. George studied mathematics, classic literature, and **surveying**.

In 1743, George's father died. George was sent to live with his brother Lawrence, a son from his father's first marriage. George worked as a surveyor. In 1749, he was **appointed** to his first public office as surveyor of Culpeper County in Virginia.

WASHINGTON'S MILITARY CAREER

In 1752, twenty year old George Washington was put in charge of the Virginia militia (muh•LIH•shuh). He trained and led his troops into the Battle of Great Meadows during the French and Indian War. After losing 100 of his men, General Washington was forced to surrender to the French.

Washington went on to serve under General Edward Braddock who had been sent by Great Britain to help the colonists win the war.

In 1755, during the Battle of the Wilderness, General Braddock was killed. Four bullets ripped through George Washington's coat, but he was not wounded. After the battle, Washington was **promoted** to colonel and named commander of the Virginia forces.

In 1759, George Washington married Martha Dandridge Custis. They moved to

YOUNG GEORGE WASHINGTON

Mount Vernon, Virginia. Black slaves were purchased to work on their huge plantation. By 1775, the Mount Vernon **estate** had grown to 6,500 acres and the Washingtons owned more than 100 slaves.

WASHINGTON'S POLITICAL CAREER

As a **respected** military hero and wealthy land owner, George Washington was elected to Virginia's House of Burgesses (BUR•jis•iz). He also served as a judge in Virginia. In 1769, Washington united with other colonists to boycott imported English goods until the Townshend Acts were repealed. In 1774, he attended the First Virginia Convention and was selected as a delegate to the First Continental Congress.

In 1775, at the Second Continental Congress, George Washington was elected by Congress to be the commander of the Continental Army. He led the United States to victory during the Revolutionary War.

In the summer of 1787, representatives from twelve states attended the Constitutional Convention at the Pennsylvania State House in Philadelphia. George Washington was elected to be in charge of the meeting.

PRESIDENT GEORGE WASHINGTON

In 1789, George Washington became the first president of the United States. During his presidency, he supported creating a national bank and taxing citizens to pay our nation's debts. Most importantly, President Washington wanted the United States to become strong and stay out of foreign wars.

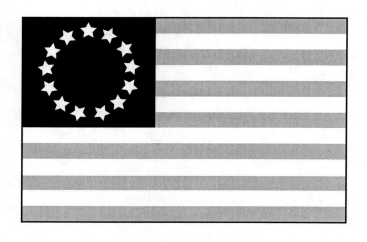

President Washington served the United States for eight years before **retiring** to his estate in Mount Vernon. Three years later, on December 14, 1799, George Washington died of a throat infection. The nation **mourned** his death for months. Even today, George Washington is remembered as one of our nation's greatest presidents.

FAST FACTS

★ George Washington was the only president who did not live in the White House.
★ Nobody ran against George Washington for president. He was elected unanimously.
★ There were 13 stars on the American flag when Washington became president. Five states were added to the Union during his presidency: North Carolina, Rhode Island, Vermont, Kentucky, and Tennessee.

Name _____

 # GEORGE WASHINGTON

Directions: Use the selection about George Washington to answer these questions. Circle the answers to questions 1 and 2. Write your answers on the lines provided for questions 3-5.

---

1 George Washington was born in 1732 and became president in 1789. How old was he when he became president?

    A 67

    B 57

    C 43

    D 41

2 After reading about George Washington, you get the idea that –

    A he was a Loyalist during the Revolutionary War

    B he was against slavery

    C he never knew what it was like to be poor

    D he was the first president to live in the White House

3 George Washington lost his first major battle of the French and Indian War, but he still went on to do great things. What can you learn about dealing with tough challenges after reading about George Washington?

_____

_____

_____

4 Are George Washington's military and political accomplishments still important to us today? Explain your answer.

_____

_____

_____

5 When you are elected president of the United States, what two positive things will you do for America?

_____

_____

_____

MAPPING: WASHINGTON, D.C

The National Mall in Washington, D.C. is the location of many important government buildings and historic points of interest. If you visited the National Mall, you would need a map to find your way around.

A **grid system** can help you locate places at the National Mall. A **grid system** is made up of lines that come together to form squares. The squares divide a map into smaller pieces, making it easier to find places. Learning how to use a **grid system** is easy, and will teach you an important location skill that you can use to find other places in the world.

Example: The Lincoln Memorial was finished in 1992, to honor President Abraham Lincoln. During the Civil War, President Lincoln fought to protect our nation and end slavery. The Lincoln Memorial is located at (6,7).

Below is a map of Constitution Gardens at the National Mall in our nation's **capital**, Washington, D.C.

Locate the Lincoln Memorial at (6,7) on the map by putting your finger on the number 1 at the bottom of the grid. Slide **over** to 6 and **up** to 7. The Lincoln Memorial is located in the square created when these two numbers come together.

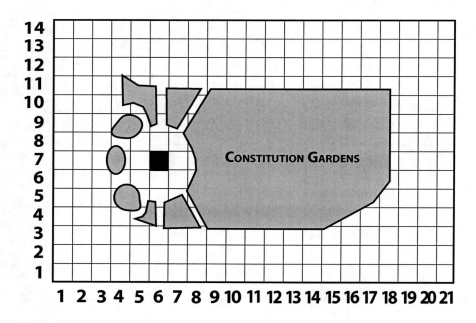

Sometimes locating a place involves two or more pairs of numbers.

Example: The Federal Reserve Board is in charge of the banking system in the United States. It makes the rules for banks and controls our money system, interest rates, and how much money can be borrowed. The Federal Reserve Board is located at (11,12) and (11,13).

Look again at the map of the Constitution Gardens at the National Mall in Washington, D.C. The Federal Reserve Board is a larger building taking up two squares on the grid. Locate the Federal Reserve Board at (11,12) on the map by putting your finger on the number 1 at the bottom of the grid.
Slide **over** to 11 and **up** to 12.

Then put your finger back on the number 1 at the bottom of the grid.
Slide **over** to 11 and **up** to 13. The Federal Reserve Board is located in the two squares created when these two number pairs come together.

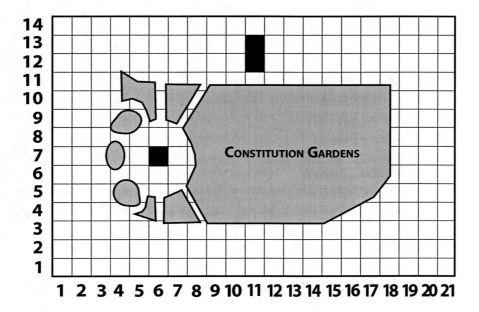

Directions: In this activity, you will use a grid system to locate many important government buildings at the National Mall in Washington, D. C.

1. Use the blank grid of the National Mall in Washington, D.C.

2. Follow the examples above for locating each important building on the grid by starting at the number 1 along the bottom and going **over** and **up**. If a building is located at (6,7), go **over** to 6 and **up** to 7.

3. Some buildings are large and can take up several squares on your grid. Make sure you locate all of the number pairs.

4. When you locate a building on the grid, color in the square or squares with a coloring pencil. You can even use a different color for each building.

1. The Department of Commerce is in charge of our **economy**. It is responsible for trade in the United States and between us and foreign countries. The Department of Commerce is also in charge of the **census** that tells us how many people are living in the United States. The Department of Commerce is located at (25,22), (25,23), (25,24), (25,25).

2. The Department of Labor helps people who have jobs by improving working conditions and making sure everyone has a safe place in which to work. The Department of Labor is located at (43,23), (44,22), (44,23), (45,23).

3. The National Museum of Natural History explores the world around us through research, education, and **exhibits**. Mammals, insects, plants, fish, and **cultures** around the world are on display at the museum. The National Museum of Natural History is located at (31,20), (32,20), (33,19), (33,20), (33,21), (34,20), (35,20).

4. The Supreme Court is the highest court in the judicial branch of the United States government. Some decisions made in lower courts can be **appealed** all the way to the Supreme Court. All decisions of the Supreme Court are final. The Supreme Court is located at (55,18), (56,18), (56,19).

5. The Washington Monument was built to honor our first president, George Washington. Completed in 1884, the Washington Monument can be seen rising high above Washington, D.C. The Washington Monument is located at (22,16).

6. The Department of Interior is responsible for managing federally owned land in the United States, **conserving** wildlife, and handling Native American concerns. The Department of Interior is located at (12,24), (12,25), (13,24), (13,25), (15,24).

7. The Senate Offices are the workplace for our nation's 100 senators who are elected to help make laws for our country. The Senate Offices are located at (53,21), (55,21), (55,22).

8. The Internal Revenue Service was created in 1862, to enforce our country's federal tax laws. It collects federal taxes, including income taxes and business taxes. The Internal Revenue Service is located at (31,23), (31,24), (32,23), (32,24).

9. The Bureau of Engraving and Printing designs, **engraves**, and prints all paper money and postage stamps. The Bureau of Engraving and Printing is located at (23,9), (23,10), (23,11), (23,12), (25,9), (25,11), (25,12), (26,9), (26,11), (26,12), (27,9), (27,11), (27,12), (28,9), (28,11), (28,12).

10. The Capitol Building is the meeting place for the legislative branch of government. Together, senators and representatives make laws for the United States of America. The Capitol Building is located at (50,17), (51,16), (51,17), (51,18).

11. The Jefferson Memorial was completed in 1943, to honor Thomas Jefferson, the author of the Declaration of Independence. Inside, visitors will find a statue of Thomas Jefferson and pieces of his famous writings. The Jefferson Memorial is located at (20,4).

12. The White House is the official home and workplace of the president of the United States. The White House is located at (18,29), (19,30), (20,30), (21,29), (21,30), (21,31).

13. The Federal Bureau of Investigation, or FBI, handles cases that involve people who are accused of breaking federal laws. The FBI is located at (34,23), (34,24).

14. The Federal Trade Commission is responsible for guaranteeing that businesses in the United States are treated fairly. It stops **monopolies** and unfair trade practices. The Federal Trade Commission is located at (40,23), (40,24), (41,23).

15. The Library of Congress is the largest library in the world. The Library of Congress includes huge collections of books on American history, music, and law. The Library of Congress is located at (55,15), (56,14), (56,15), (56,16).

16. The Department of Treasury is in charge of everything that concerns our nation's money. The Department of Treasury is located at (23,29), (24,29), (24,30), (25,29), (25,30).

17. The Department of Justice provides legal advice to the president of the United States and other officials. It also represents the United States in court and enforces most federal criminal and **civil** laws. The Department of Justice is located at (34,26),(34,27).

18.   The National Postal Museum tells the story of postal history in America. It is inside of the City Post Office, which has served as the Washington, D.C. post office for 72 years. The National Postal Museum is located at (27,22), (28,22), (29,22), (29,23), (29,24).

19.   The Department of State protects the United States in foreign activities. This includes helping United States citizens who travel or do business in foreign countries. The Department of State also keeps us informed about our relationships with other countries. The Department of State is located at (6,24), (6,25), (7,24), (7,25).

20.   The National Museum of American History collects and preserves more than three million **artifacts** from American history. Exhibits at the museum explore our nation's wars, leaders, and famous people. The National Museum of American History is located at (27,19), (27,20), (28,19), (28,20).

21.   The House Offices are the workplace for members of the House of Representatives who are elected to help make laws for our country. The House Offices are located at (49,12), (51,11), (51,12), (52,11), (53,12).

22.   The National **Archives** protect and display important documents relating to the history and people of the United States. The National Archives are located at (36,24), (37,23), (37,24), (37,25), (38,24).

23.   The National Gallery of Art was created in 1937, with a generous gift from art collector Andrew W. Mellon. **Donations** of art and money from others over the years have formed an art gallery that visitors from all over the United States travel to see. The National Gallery of Art is located at (38,20), (38,21), (39,20), (40,19), (40,20), (40,21), (41,20).

24.   The Department of Health and Human Services is in charge of helping the poorest citizens in the United States with **welfare** and public health programs. The Department of Health and Human Services is located at (39,11), (40,11), (41,11), (41,12), (42,11), (42,12).

National Mall Washington, D.C.

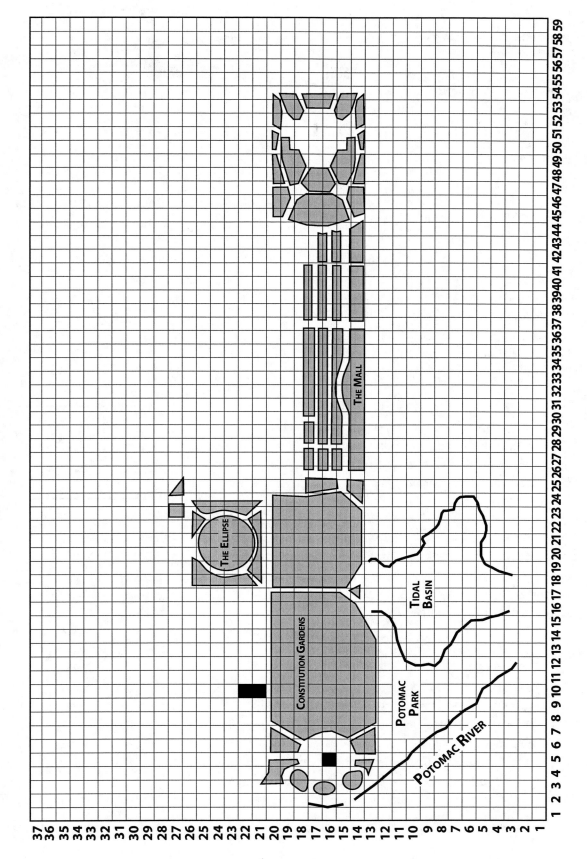

The Mall

The Ellipse

Constitution Gardens

Tidal Basin

Potomac Park

Potomac River

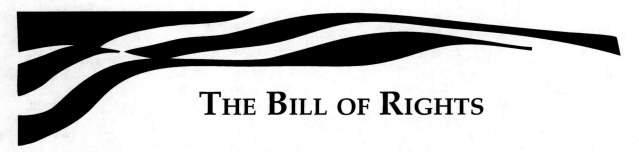

THE BILL OF RIGHTS

In 1789, George Washington became the first president of the United States. During his presidency, our nation went through many changes. The biggest change involved the newly written Constitution.

The United States Constitution had been in effect for less than a year when George Washington became president. There were already changes to be made.

The citizens of the United States were afraid that a strong government would take away their rights. The people wanted the United States Constitution to clearly list these rights so that they would be protected from a government that became too powerful.

THE BILL OF RIGHTS

On June 8, 1789, the first Congress under President George Washington met in New York City. Guided by James Madison, Congress wrote the first ten **amendments** to the United States Constitution. These amendments are known as the Bill of Rights.

The changes to the United States Constitution clearly list certain freedoms that the federal and state governments can not take away. The First Amendment includes freedom of speech, freedom of the **press**, and freedom for people to gather peacefully and worship as they please. The Second Amendment includes the right to have and carry weapons.

LIMITING THE GOVERNMENT

The Bill of Rights also limits the power of the government over people. The Third Amendment guarantees that citizens will not be forced to keep soldiers in their homes during times of peace like they had been forced to do before the Revolutionary War.

Under the Fourth Amendment, the police can not search a person's home or take property without a **warrant**.

PRESIDENT GEORGE WASHINGTON

A warrant can only be issued by a judge. Before a judge can issue a warrant for a search, the police must present facts to prove that a crime has actually been committed.

PROTECTION FOR THE PEOPLE

The first ten amendments also include rights for people who are accused of a crime. The Fifth Amendment states that a person accused of a crime does not have to **testify** against himself. If found **innocent** of a crime, the Fifth Amendment guarantees that the accused person can not be blamed again for that same crime. The Fifth Amendment also stops the government from taking a person's property and using it for public purposes unless the government pays for the property.

The Sixth Amendment states that people who are arrested have the right to be told for what crime they are being blamed. Further, anyone accused of a crime is guaranteed a speedy and public trial with a jury. The accused person also has the right to have a lawyer to help defend him or her.

The Seventh Amendment guarantees a jury trial for someone who is being **sued** for money. The Eighth Amendment states that **bail** for an accused person has to reasonable. If found guilty, the punishment for the crime can not be cruel and unusual.

MORE ROOM FOR CHANGE

The Ninth and Tenth amendments of the Bill of Rights are especially important. They speak of the biggest fear of all people in the United States. Throughout the entire process of writing and approving the United States Constitution, the people were afraid of a federal government that would become too powerful. They didn't want to be treated unfairly the way Great Britain had treated them.

The Ninth Amendment states that people have other rights than those listed in the United States Constitution. The Tenth Amendment guarantees that powers not granted to the federal government will be given to the state governments or to the people. These two amendments let us know that the United States Constitution is not finished. For this reason, the Constitution is known as a "living document." When the Constitution was written, the United States was a new country that would go through many changes. As other rights and freedoms need to be added, Congress will have to write amendments for them.

FAST FACTS

★ The First Amendment is considered to be the most important. It protects our freedom of religion, speech, and the right to gather and ask our government to make changes to laws.
★ There were originally twelve amendments to the United States Constitution. Only ten of them were approved by Congress.
★ The Bill of Rights was adopted on December 15, 1791. The anniversary of the Bill of Rights is celebrated on September 25. This is the day that Congress actually finished the Bill of Rights.

Name _____

Directions: Read each question carefully. Darken the circle for the correct answer.

1 **Why was it necessary to create the Bill of Rights?**

   A Women wanted the right to vote.

   B The United States was afraid of going to war with Great Britain again.

   C The United States government wanted to be able to take certain rights away from the citizens.

   D The citizens of the United States were afraid that a strong government would take away their rights.

2 **What is protected by the First Amendment?**

   F Freedom of speech.

   G Freedom to carry weapons.

   H Freedom to break laws that we don't like.

   J Freedom to know what crime you are being accused of.

3 **Which amendment protects us from having to feed and house soldiers like the colonists had been forced to do during colonial days?**

   A First Amendment

   B Second Amendment

   C Third Amendment

   D Fourth Amendment

4 **The Bill of Rights limits the power of the –**

   F people

   G government

   H Native Americans

   J explorers

5 **The Bill of Rights includes the first ten amendments to the Constitution. Amendments are –**

   A people

   B promises

   C rights

   D changes

6 **Which of the following is an example of a Secondary Source?**

   F The pen used to sign the Bill of Rights.

   G An interview with George Washington.

   H A movie written about the Constitution and the Bill of Rights.

   J The signed copy of the Bill of Rights displayed at the National Archives.

7 **Why is the United States Constitution known as a "living document?"**

   A It was written by people who are still alive today.

   B It is alive in our hearts and minds.

   C It is always changing and never finished.

   D It protects only people who are living.

READING

Answers

1 Ⓐ Ⓑ Ⓒ Ⓓ   5 Ⓐ Ⓑ Ⓒ Ⓓ
2 Ⓕ Ⓖ Ⓗ Ⓙ   6 Ⓕ Ⓖ Ⓗ Ⓙ
3 Ⓐ Ⓑ Ⓒ Ⓓ   7 Ⓐ Ⓑ Ⓒ Ⓓ
4 Ⓕ Ⓖ Ⓗ Ⓙ

  LET'S TALK ABOUT IT

THE BILL OF RIGHTS

The Bill of Rights gave Americans the guarantee that their rights and freedoms would always be protected. Read the questions below about the Bill of Rights. Write your answers on the lines provided. Attach a separate piece of paper if you need more room. Be ready to discuss some of your answers.

• **The Bill of Rights includes ten amendments to the Constitution. Each amendment guarantees important freedoms for Americans.**

What right is guaranteed by the Third Amendment? Do you think this is an important right for us to have today? Explain your answer.

_____

_____

_____

In your own words, describe the rights guaranteed in the Sixth Amendment. Do you think these are important rights? Explain.

_____

_____

_____

• **The First Amendment includes freedom of speech, freedom of the press, and freedom for people to gather peacefully and worship as they please.**

Most people think that the First Amendment is the most important. Do you agree? Why or why not?

_____

_____

_____

Name _____

✪ ✯ ✩ ✦✯ VOCABULARY QUIZ ✪ ✯ ✩ ✦✯

EARLY AMERICAN GOVERNMENT
PART V

Directions: Match the vocabulary word on the left with its definition on the right. Put the letter for the definition on the blank next to the vocabulary word it matches. Use each word and definition only once.

1. _____ warrant

2. _____ testify

3. _____ sued

4. _____ welfare

5. _____ Supreme Court

6. _____ ratify

7. _____ amendments

8. _____ innocent

9. _____ bail

10. _____ abused

11. _____ press

12. _____ population

13. _____ appealed

14. _____ plantations

15. _____ archives

16. _____ outlawed

17. _____ artifacts

A. money given by the government to people who need help.

B. free gifts given to someone in need.

C. to make a formal statement in court about what is true.

D. carves or cuts a design or letters into something.

E. expressed deep sadness.

F. objects and tools used by early humans for eating, cooking, and hunting.

G. a word used to describe the way a city, town, state, or country makes money.

H. changes in wording or meaning.

I. moved up in rank.

J. types of laws that affect the rights of people.

K. made it illegal to do something.

L. signed permission from a judge to arrest or search someone's property.

M. disagreed with a court's ruling; asked a higher court to make a decision on the same case.

N. money needed to free a person charged with a crime from jail until he or she goes to trial.

O. fairness in the court system.

P. people responsible for reporting the news.

18. _____ census

19. _____ monopolies

20. _____ justice

21. _____ civil

22. _____ conserving

23. _____ cultures

24. _____ illegal

25. _____ exhibits

26. _____ helium

27. _____ donations

28. _____ economy

29. _____ engraves

30. _____ surveying

31. _____ appointed

32. _____ promoted

33. _____ estate

34. _____ respected

35. _____ retiring

36. _____ mourned

37. _____ capital

38. _____ convinced

Q. an official count of the number of people in a place.

R. very large farms in the South where crops of cotton and tobacco were grown and slave labor was usually used.

S. leaving a job permanently to rest or try something else.

T. went to court in the hopes of winning a judgment against someone for wrong doing.

U. measuring land.

V. used incorrectly.

W. groups of people with a shared set of beliefs, goals, religious customs, attitudes, and social practices.

X. the city that serves as the center of government for the state or nation.

Y. places where public records or other historical documents are kept.

Z. the highest court in the state or nation.

AA. talked someone into doing something your way.

BB. companies or groups that have complete control over a product or service.

CC. the total number of people living in an area.

DD. a very light gas which does not burn.

EE. large country home on a big piece of land.

FF. highly honored.

GG. using something carefully so it won't be wasted or used up too quickly.

HH. chosen or selected.

II. approve.

JJ. displays.

KK. not guilty.

LL. against the law.

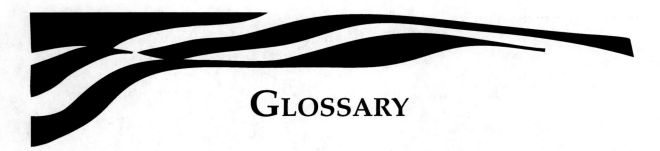

GLOSSARY

a•bol•ish stop or put an end to.

a•bused used incorrectly.

ac•cused blamed or charged with a crime.

a•dopt accept and put into action.

al•lies groups of people who come together to help one another in times of trouble.

am•bushed attacked by surprise.

a•mend•ments changes in wording or meaning.

an•cient a very long time ago.

ap•pealed disagreed with a court's ruling; asked a higher court to make a decision on the same case.

ap•point•ed chosen or selected.

ar•chae•ol•o•gists scientists who study past human life by looking at prehistoric fossils and tools.

ar•chi•tects people who design buildings.

ar•chives places where public records or other historical documents are kept.

ar•ti•facts objects and tools used by early humans for eating, cooking, and hunting.

A•sia the world's largest continent with more than half of the Earth's population.

At•lan•tic Coast the area of land that borders the Atlantic Ocean.

au•to•bi•og•ra•phy the story of your life written by you.

bail money needed to free a person charged with a crime from jail until he or she goes to trial.

bi•og•ra•phies stories of a person's life written by someone else.

bound•a•ries dividing lines.

boy•cot•ting refusing to buy.

cap•i•tal the city that serves as the center of government for the state or nation.

cap•tives prisoners who have been taken without permission.

cen•sus an official count of the number of people in a place.

cen•tu•ries periods of 100 years.

char•ters contracts which give one group power over another.

Church of En•gland the official church in England.

cit•i•zen a person in a city, town, state, or country who enjoys the freedom to vote and participate in government decisions.

civ•il types of laws that affect the rights of people.

col•o•nists people who are ruled by another country.

com•mis•sion•ers government officials in charge of a department.

con•fed•er•a•cy a group of people with common goals.

con•flicts struggles or disagreements.

con•serv•ing using something carefully so it won't be wasted or used up too quickly.

con•sti•tu•tion a plan that outlines the duties of government and guarantees the rights of the people.

Con•ti•nen•tal Ar•my American troops that fought against Great Britain during the Revolutionary War.

coun•cil a group of people chosen to make laws or give advice.

con•vinced talked someone into doing something your way.

cul•ti•vate to prepare the soil for growing crops.

cul•tures groups of people with a shared set of beliefs, goals, religious customs, attitudes, and social practices.

de•bate a discussion that gives arguments for and against a subject.

debt money that is owed to someone else.

de•feat to win victory over.

de•fend to keep safe from danger, attack, or harm.

del•e•gates people sent with power to represent others.

de•moc•ra•cy a type of government that gives the people the power to elect leaders who will make and enforce laws.

dis•crim•i•nat•ed treated some people better or worse than others without a good reason.

dis•guised changed appearance to keep from being recognized.

do•na•tions free gifts given to someone in need.

e•con•o•my a word used to describe the way a city, town, state, or country makes money.

e•lec•ted selected leaders by voting for them.

en•force require someone to obey the rules.

en•graves carves or cuts a design or letters into something.

es•tate large country home on a big piece of land.

Eu•ro•pe•an a person who comes from the continent of Europe.

ex•hib•its displays.

fed•er•al gov•ern•ment the group of people at the national level elected to set up a system of rules and laws for our country.

for•eign from another country or nation.

found•ed started or established.

fun•gus a disease that destroys plants.

gov•er•nor a person who is in charge of an area or group.

Great Lakes five large lakes located in North America at the border between Canada and the United States. The names of the lakes are Superior, Michigan, Huron, Erie, and Ontario.

grist•mills mills for grinding grain into flour.

harsh very uncomfortable conditions.

he•li•um a very light gas which does not burn.

his•to•ri•ans people who study the past.

hos•til•i•ty anger and unfriendliness.

ig•nored didn't listen to.

il•le•gal against the law.

im•port•ed types of items brought into a country for the purpose of selling them.

in•come money earned from doing work or owning property.

in•de•pen•dent not being under the control or rule of someone else.

in•di•go a plant which produces a blue dye.

in•hab•it•ed lived or settled in a place.

in•no•cent not guilty.

in•ter•fere to become involved when help is not wanted.

in•tol•er•a•ble impossible to put up with; unable to bear.

ju•ry a group of people who are chosen to listen to all of the facts during a court case before making a judgment for guilt or innocence.

jus•tice fairness in the court system.

long•hous•es long dwellings where many Native American families live at the same time.

loy•al•ty faithfulness.

maize a type of corn.

ma•jor•i•ty more than half.

mer•chants buyers and sellers whose goal is to make money.

mil•i•tar•y people who are part of the armed forces who may be asked to go to war.

mi•li•tia a group of men having some military training who are called upon only in emergencies.

min•ute•men groups of armed men who were prepared to fight on a minute's notice during the Revolutionary War.

mon•arch a king, queen, or emperor who rules for his or her entire life and then passes the role onto his or her child.

mo•nop•o•lies companies or groups that have complete control over a product or service.

mourned expressed deep sadness.

New Eng•land a region in the northeast corner of the United States that includes Connecticut, Maine, Massachusetts, New Hampshire, Rhode Island, and Vermont.

New France French colonies in North America that were given to Great Britain after the French and Indian War.

New World a term once used to describe the continents of North America and South America.

North A•mer•i•ca one of seven continents in the world. Bounded by Alaska on the northwest, Greenland on the northeast, Florida on the southeast, and Mexico on the southwest.

of•fi•cial proper or correct.

out•lawed made it illegal to do something.

out•raged angered beyond belief.

o•ver•turn to destroy the power of; to defeat.

Pa•tri•ots people who supported the United States during the Revolutionary War.

Pil•grims the English colonists who founded the first permanent settlement in the New England colony of Plymouth in 1620.

plan•ta•tions very large farms in the South where crops of cotton and tobacco were grown and slave labor was usually used.

pop•u•la•tion the total number of people living in an area.

pre•serve protect from injury or ruin so more can be learned.

press people responsible for reporting the news.

proc•la•ma•tion an official announcement.

pro•fit money made after all expenses have been paid.

pro•hib•it•ed not allowed.

pro•mot•ed moved up in rank.

pros•per to have success or wealth.

pro•test to argue against something thought to be unfair.

prov•ince a part of a country having a government of its own.

Pu•ri•tan a person from England who traveled to America in the 1600s and 1700s in search of religious freedom.

Qua•kers members of a religious group who believed all men were created equal, refused to serve in the army or navy, and would not pay taxes used to support war.

raid•ed entered someone's property to steal from them.

rat•i•fy approve.

reb•el to battle against authority.

re•pealed done away with; removed.

rep•re•sen•ta•tive a person chosen to speak or act for an entire group.

re•served set aside for a special purpose.

re•sourc•es things found in nature that are valuable to humans.

re•spect•ed highly honored.

re•tir•ing leaving a job permanently to rest or try something else.

re•volt•ed battled against rules and laws felt to be unfair.

Rev•o•lu•tion•ar•y War battle for independence between the English colonists in America and Great Britain.

saw•mills businesses with big machines that saw wood into planks and boards.

seized took by force.

sued went to court in the hopes of winning a judgment against someone for wrong doing.

Su•preme Court the highest court in the state or nation.

sur•ren•dered gave up.

sur•vey•ing measuring land.

tes•ti•fy to make a formal statement in court about what is true.

trai•tors people who do things to hurt their countries.

trans•port•ed moved products or people from one place to another.

u•nan•i•mous•ly completely agreed upon by everyone.

u•nit•ed joined together and formed a single unit.

ve•toed prevented a bill from becoming a law.

voy•age journey that is usually made by water.

war•rant signed permission from a judge to arrest or search someone's property.

wel•fare money given by the government to people who need help.

wig•wam a Native American home made of poles and covered with bark, mats, or animal skins.

ANSWERS

ANSWERS TO COMPREHENSION QUESTIONS

GOVERNMENT

1. C
2. G
3. C
4. G
5. D
6. H
7. C

FIRST GOVERNMENTS IN AMERICA

1. C
2. G
3. C
4. F
5. C
6. F
7. D

FRENCH AND INDIAN WAR

1. A
2. J
3. B
4. H
5. C
6. J
7. D

GREAT BRITAIN'S TAXES

1. D
2. G
3. C
4. G
5. A
6. H
7. B

THE CONTINENTAL CONGRESS

1. C
2. J
3. A
4. H
5. C
6. J
7. B

THE DECLARATION OF INDEPENDENCE

1. A
2. H
3. D
4. G
5. C
6. G
7. B

THE ARTICLES OF CONFEDERATION

1. D
2. H
3. D
4. J
5. A
6. H
7. C

THE UNITED STATES CONSTITUTION

1. C
2. H
3. C
4. G
5. D
6. J
7. A

GEORGE WASHINGTON

1. B
2. C
3. Answers will vary.
4. Answers will vary.
5. Answers will vary.

THE BILL OF RIGHTS

1. D
2. F
3. C
4. G
5. D
6. H
7. C

CONSIDER THE SOURCE

1. S
2. P
3. P
4. P
5. P
6. P
7. S

ANSWERS TO VOCABULARY QUIZZES

PART I	PART II	PART III	PART IV	PART V
1. Q	1. E	1. J	1. Y	1. L
2. H	2. O	2. D	2. A	2. C
3. A	3. AA	3. U	3. V	3. T
4. S	4. H	4. B	4. X	4. A
5. K	5. K	5. O	5. F	5. Z
6. D	6. Z	6. T	6. R	6. II
7. M	7. R	7. R	7. I	7. H
8. O	8. DD	8. C	8. M	8. KK
9. I	9. A	9. W	9. N	9. N
10. C	10. Q	10. F	10. C	10. V
11. R	11. W	11. L	11. AA	11. P
12. F	12. T	12. P	12. T	12. CC
13. B	13. Y	13. E	13. K	13. M
14. E	14. P	14. M	14. P	14. R
15. L	15. CC	15. S	15. B	15. Y
16. J	16. EE	16. A	16. U	16. K
17. N	17. U	17. Q	17. E	17. F
18. G	18. F	18. H	18. L	18. Q
19. P	19. M	19. N	19. W	19. BB
	20. BB	20. K	20. G	20. O
	21. C	21. I	21. Q	21. J
	22. S	22. G	22. D	22. GG
	23. B	23. V	23. J	23. W
	24. G		24. S	24. LL
	25. L		25. H	25. JJ
	26. FF		26. Z	26. DD
	27. I		27. O	27. B
	28. J		28. BB	28. G
	29. D			29. D
	30. X			30. U
	31. N			31. HH
	32. V			32. I
				33. EE
				34. FF
				35. S
				36. E
				37. X
				38. AA

ANSWERS TO TIME TRAVEL

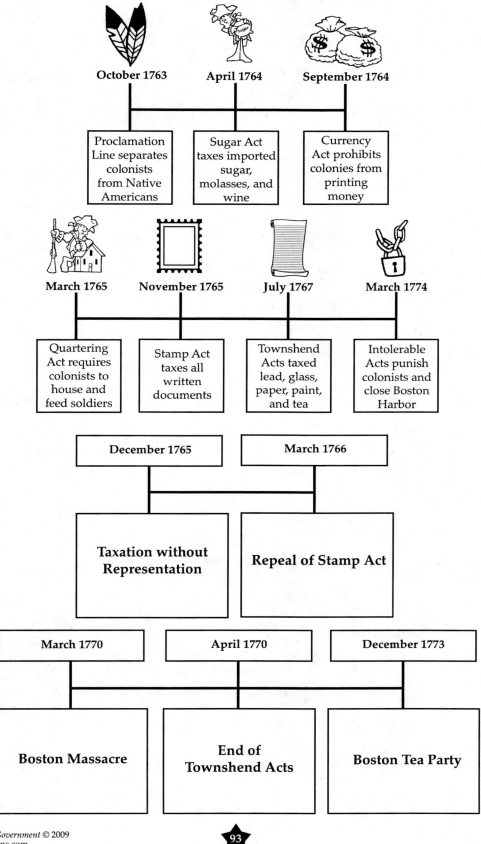

October 1763   **April 1764**   **September 1764**

| Proclamation Line separates colonists from Native Americans | Sugar Act taxes imported sugar, molasses, and wine | Currency Act prohibits colonies from printing money |

March 1765   **November 1765**   **July 1767**   **March 1774**

| Quartering Act requires colonists to house and feed soldiers | Stamp Act taxes all written documents | Townshend Acts taxed lead, glass, paper, paint, and tea | Intolerable Acts punish colonists and close Boston Harbor |

December 1765   **March 1766**

Taxation without Representation   **Repeal of Stamp Act**

March 1770   **April 1770**   **December 1773**

Boston Massacre   **End of Townshend Acts**   **Boston Tea Party**

ANSWERS TO FRENCH AND INDIAN WAR MAPPING

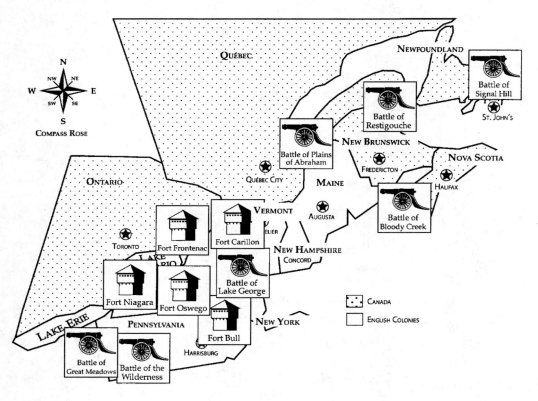

ANSWERS TO WASHINGTON, D.C. MAPPING

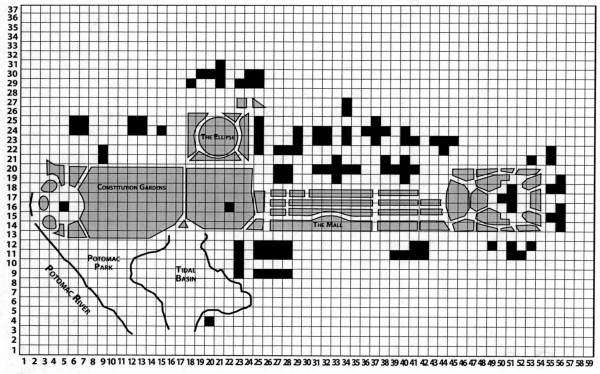

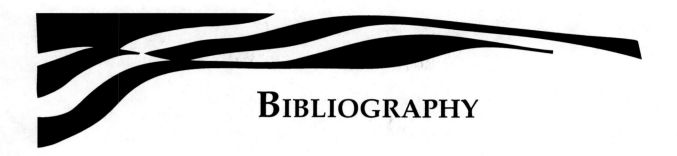

BIBLIOGRAPHY

American Heritage Dictionary of the English Language, Fourth Edition, Houghton Mifflin, Massachusetts, 2000.

AmericanRevolution.com: 'The American Revolution' 2006 [Online]
Available <http://www.americanrevolution.com/> (December 17, 2008)

Bartleby: 'American Heritage Dictionary of the English Language: Fourth Edition' 2000 [Online]
Available <http://www.bartleby.com> (August 23, 2007)

Baranzini, Marlene and Bovert, Howard (1995), *US Kids History Book of the New American Nation*, Yolla Bolly Press, California

Bent, Devin: 'Constitutional Convention Overview' 2007 [Online]
Available <http://www.jmu.edu/madison/gpos225-madison2/adopt.htm> (September 4, 2008)

Carter, Alden R. (1988), *Birth of the Republic*, Frank Watts, New York

Fradin, Dennis (1990), *The Connecticut Colony*, Children's Press, Chicago

Fradin, Dennis (1992), *The Delaware Colony*, Children's Press, Chicago

Fradin, Dennis (1990), *The Georgia Colony*, Children's Press, Chicago

Fradin, Dennis (1990), *The Maryland Colony*, Children's Press, Chicago

Fradin, Dennis (1987), *The Massachusetts Colony*, Regensteiner and Children's Press, Chicago

Fradin, Dennis (1988), *The New Hampshire Colony*, Children's Press, Chicago

Fradin, Dennis (1991), *The New Jersey Colony*, Children's Press, Chicago

Fradin, Dennis (1988), *The New York Colony*, Children's Press, Chicago

Fradin, Dennis (1991), *The North Carolina Colony*, Children's Press, Chicago

Fradin, Dennis (1988), *The Pennsylvania Colony*, Regensteiner and Children's Press, Chicago

Fradin, Dennis (1989), *The Rhode Island Colony*, Children's Press, Chicago

Fradin, Dennis (1995), *Rhode Island: From Sea to Shining Sea*, Children's Press, Chicago

Fradin, Dennis and Judith (1992), *The South Carolina Colony*, Children's Press, Connecticut

Geology.com: 'US Map Collections' 2008 [Online]
Available <http://geology.com/state-map/> (December 3, 2008)

Headley, Amy and Smith, Victoria. (2003), *Do American History!* Splash! Publications, Arizona

Holypark Media: 'Facts You May not Know about the Boston Tea Party' 2008 [Online]
Available <http://www.boston-tea-party.org/unknown-facts.html> (Februray 22, 2009)

Hooker, Richard: 'The Iroquois League' 1996 [Online]
Available <http://www.wsu.edu/~dee/CULAMRCA/IRLEAGUE.HTM> (January 2, 2009)

Houdman, M. and Matthews-Rose, R: 'The Mayflower Compact' 2008 [Online]
Available <http://www.allabouthistory.org/mayflower-compact.htm> (March 28, 2008)

Independence Hall Association: 'Congress' 2008 [Online]
Available <http://www.ushistory.org/declaration/related/congress.htm> (February 2, 2009)

Independence Hall Association: 'Carpenters' Hall' 2008 [Online]
    Available <http://www.ushistory.org/tour/tour_carpen.htm> (February 2, 2009)
Internet School Library Media Center: 'Colonial America 1600-1775 K12 Resources' 2003 [Online]
    Available <http://falcon.jmu.edu/~ramseyil/colonial.htm#A> (March 10, 2008)
Isaacs, Sally Senzell (1998), *America in the Time of Pocahontas*, Heinemann Library, Illinois
Kent, Zachary (1986), *Encyclopedia of Presidents: George Washington*, Regensteiner, Chicago
Kidport: 'The Second Continental Congress' 2007 [Online] Available
    <http://www.kidport.com/RefLib/UsaHistory/AmericanRevolution/SecondCongress.htm>
    (April 6, 2008)
Klos, Stanley: 'Articles of Confederation' 2000 [Online] Available
    <http://thedeclarationofindependence.org/articlesofconfederation.com/> (February 10, 2009)
Lee, John and Susan (1974), *George Washington*, Regensteiner, Chicago
Lexico Publishing Group: 'Dictionary.com' 2004 [Online]
    Available <http:// dictionary.reference.com/> (September 1, 2008)
Lukes, Bonnie L. (1996), *The American Revolution*, Lucent Books, California
Maps.com: 'Maine Historical Map: French and Indian War 1754-1763' 2007 [Online]
    Available <http://www.maps.com/ref_map.aspx?pid=11841> (November 4, 2008)
Miller, Judy: 'George Washington Trivia' 2008 [Online] Available <http://www.apples4theteacher.
    com/holidays/presidents-day/george-washington/facts.html> (January 4, 2009)
Missouri Bar: 'Amazing Facts About the Constitution' 2006 [Online]
    Available <http://members.mobar.org/civics/Facts.htm (January 6, 2009)
MultiEducator, Inc: 'U.S. Civics: How the U.S. Government Works' 2000 [Online]
    Available <http://www.historycentral.com/Civics/Index.html> (March 7, 2009)
NativeAmericans.com: 'Native Americans' 2007 [Online]
    Available <http://www.nativeamericans.com/Natives.htm> (November 8, 2008)
Nussbaum, Greg: 'Revolutionary War' 2005 [Online]
    Available <http://www.mrnussbaum.com/amflash.htm> (November 2, 2008)
Online Highways: 'Colonial America First Continental Congress, 1774' [Online]
    Available <http://www.u-s-history.com/pages/h650.html> (December 5, 2008)
Philadelphia Yearly Meeting: 'Penn's Holy Experiment: The Seed of a Nation' 2001 [Online] Available
    <http://www.pym.org/exhibit/p078.html> (January 21, 2009)
Smithsonian Institution: 'The National Postal Museum' 2008 [Online]
    Available <http://www.postalmuseum.si.edu/museum/1c_history.html> (February 8, 2009)
Sobel, Syl (1996), *How the U.S. Government Works*, Barron's Educational Series, Inc., New York
Stites, Bill (2005), *Democracy, A Primary Source Analysis*, The Rosen Publishing Group, Inc., New York
Webster's Revised Unabridged Dictionary, MICRA, New Jersey, 1998.
White, David: 'The Articles of Confederation' 2008 [Online] Available
    <http://www.socialstudiesforkids.com/articles/ushistory/articlesofconfederation1.htm>
    (July 8, 2008)
White House, The: 'George Washington' 2008 [Online]
    Available <http://www.whitehouse.gov/history/presidents/gw1.html> (August 9, 2008)
Zeman, Ann and Kelly, Kate (1994), *Everything You Need to Know about American History Homework*,
    Scholastic, Inc., New York